# STEVENGRAPHS

# STEVENGRAPHS

The Reference Book on Thomas Stevens'
mounted silk woven pictures and silk woven
bookmarkers


PART I
The Mounted Silk Woven Pictures and Portraits
by *Austin Sprake*, M.A., LL.B.


PART II
The Silk Woven Bookmarkers
by *Michael Darby*


1968

Published in Guernsey by the authors to
commemorate the 90th anniversary of the
first mounted Stevens' silk pictures in 1879.

*1st Edition*, 1968 ©

181

*Printed in Great Britain by*
*Fletcher & Son Ltd, Norwich*
*and bound by Richard Clay (The Chaucer Press) Ltd,*
*Bungay, Suffolk*

# CONTENTS

# ACKNOWLEDGEMENTS

## STEVENGRAPHS

I am most grateful to Mrs L. G. Nicoll, Mr A. G. H. Goodhart, and Mr B. W. Blades, for kindly letting me examine their collections, to Mr Cyril Scott, Curator of the Herbert Art Gallery and Museum, Coventry, for allowing me to study the Museum's collection and for helping over photographs, and to Mr Lewis Smith who gave the books containing an almost complete photographic record of Stevengraphs to the Coventry Museum, which I have studied on several occasions and found most helpful, and who helped with supplying photographs and other information contained in this book. I must also record my thanks to Mr Jack Guy of Messrs Knight Frank & Rutley, Mr Alastair Leslie and Mrs Anne Munton for their encouragement and assistance in many ways. I am particularly indebted to Mrs Mary Migotti for allowing me to photograph specimens from her collection prior to its sale. These photographs together with ones taken from my own collection and from the Coventry Museum's collection and ones kindly provided by Mr Smith, Mr Blades and Mr Goodhart are reproduced in this book.

I would like to take the opportunity to thank once again all those people who from time to time sell Stevengraphs to me which have helped to form the basis of my own collection. I shall always be pleased to hear from any person who has a Stevengraph which appears to be unlisted in this book so that it can be recorded and possibly photographed in colour for a special centenary edition in 1979.

c/o Barclays Bank Ltd.,
St. Peter Port,        AUSTIN SPRAKE
Guernsey          *March 1968*

## BOOKMARKERS

I am indebted to Mrs L. G. Nicoll, the late Miss R. Berney and Mr Alastair Leslie for letting me study their collections of bookmarkers and particularly to Mr C. J. Scott, Curator of the Herbert

ACKNOWLEDGEMENTS

Art Gallery and Museum, Coventry, for his co-operation in allowing me to examine the Museum's collection. The photographs of bookmarkers appearing in this book were taken from Mr Leslie's large collection. I must also thank Mr Lewis Smith of New York for his assistance by way of providing the excellent photographic records of bookmarkers housed in the Coventry Museum.

I shall be pleased to hear from any reader who possesses a bookmarker which does not appear to be recorded in this book so that it may be noted for inclusion in the next edition.

c/o The Textile Department,                    MICHAEL DARBY
Victoria and Albert Museum,                      *March 1968*
London, S.W.7.

# INTRODUCTION

Mr. Gladstone in his speech referring to Stevens' productions, said "Coventry under pressure has discovered such excellence, skill, and resources, as I venture to say, any manufacturer thirty years ago would have said was impossible."—*Daily Telegraph*, Nov. 2nd, 1870.

The weaving of fancy silk ribbons began in Coventry around 1700 and almost came to an abrupt end in 1860 when the industry suffered a disastrous slump as a result of the Government removing the prohibition on imported silk goods. Cheap foreign wares flooded into England, and most of the Coventry weavers were forced out of business.

Thomas Stevens had already been working in the silk weaving trade all his life, and in 1854 he had set up his own business. He was experimenting with new ideas and improved techniques before the slump, and when this came he accepted the challenge it presented. He succeeded in adapting the Jacquard loom to produce small multi-coloured silk pictures of infinite variety, and, in 1863, when most other Coventry weavers had packed up, he sold his first silk woven bookmarkers. These were an immediate success and soon afterwards he developed the idea of selling similar things made up in the form of Christmas and birthday greeting cards, Valentine cards, calendars, sashes and badges.

In no time Stevens had created for himself an entirely new market, with sales through booksellers and stationers, as opposed to selling to the drapery trade, for which market all Coventry brocades and ribbons had previously been produced. The bookmarkers depicted contemporary scenes, portraits of royalty and notables, illuminated texts from the Bible, poems, seasonal and birthday greetings.

In 1879 Stevens produced his gay little pictures in yet another form. He fitted them into simple cardboard mounts all ready for framing and hanging in the home. The striking three-dimensional effect of these mounted silk pictures helped to give them instant success, and over the ensuing thirty years thousands upon thousands were sold. Stevens died in London in 1888 from where he had been directing the business for several years, while his two sons ran the factory in Coventry, but the business remained in family

1

hands for another twenty years until it was made a limited company in 1908. About this time a number of the silk pictures were produced in miniature form and sold as postcards. Although few of these bore his name, they can be identified as his quite easily owing to being so similar to his mounted pictures.

As 1914 approached and fashions changed, the demand for bookmarkers, silk pictures and fancy novelties dwindled, and although the factory remained in business producing other silk articles until it was totally destroyed in the Coventry blitz of 1940, only a very few silk pictures were made in the 'twenties and 'thirties. The portraits of King George VI and Queen Elizabeth (the Queen Mother) made in 1938, some of which were made in the form of calendars, were probably the last silk pictures ever produced at the factory.

Stevens set up portable looms at many of the large trade exhibitions in Britain, on the Continent and in America, and visitors were able to watch the pictures being woven, and were invited to make purchases then and there. The first place at which Stevens exhibited looms weaving pictures, which were actually mounted and sold on the spot, was the York Exhibition of 1879.

A large number of pictures of all subjects were exported to America by Stevens, which accounts for their popularity amongst American collectors today.

Some indication of the order in which the various titles were produced can be obtained from their position on the list of titles found on the trade label stuck to the back of most pictures. A diamond shaped registration mark is found on the labels of early examples, while a similar shaped mark is found impressed on the front of the mount of some pictures. Both marks were discontinued soon after 1879. The firm became a limited company in 1908 so any pictures bearing Stevens' identification which incorporates the word "Ltd." indicates post 1908 manufacture. It must be emphasised that these rough dating clues only indicate when the picture was mounted and sold, not necessarily when it was woven, because the pictures were woven in long rolls or bolts, some of which were immediately cut up and mounted for selling, while the remaining bolts were put into store for future use.

These little Victorian novelties woven with such three-dimen-

2

sional effect do not appeal to everyone but a collection of them gives cheer to an empty wall, pleasure to a receptive eye, and provides the diligent searcher with something fresh to look for and no doubt with a sound investment.

Readers interested in further background information on Thomas Stevens, his family and silk weaving in general should read the early part of Mrs Le Van Baker's book "The Silk Pictures of Thomas Stevens", Exposition Press, New York.

(The Introduction is reproduced from an article by Austin Sprake which appeared in the *Antique Dealer and Collector's Guide*, February 1968.)

# THE MOUNTED SILK WOVEN PICTURES
## AND PORTRAITS

*Stevengraphs*

This trade name was coined by Thomas Stevens about 1863 and was intended to describe any of his woven articles, but today it is taken only to refer to his mounted silk pictures and portraits. When they left the factory the pictures and portraits were in cardboard mounts nearly always with Stevens' trade label stuck to the back and with his name and the title printed on the front. Bookmarkers left the factory pinned to a paper backing, often with Stevens' trademark printed or embossed at the top of the backing.

*Stevens' Identification*

In most cases Stevens' name was printed on the front of the mount, e.g. "woven in silk by Thomas Stevens, Coventry and London, Registered". Sometimes this is abbreviated simply to "woven in pure silk", particularly on late versions. Specimens are often found with no wording at all on the front and these were probably trade samples not intended for retail sale. Stevens' trade label listing other subjects available for sale, usually appears stuck to the back although it is missing on occasional specimens, again possibly because they were intended as trade samples.

Certain Stevengraphs did not normally possess the usual trade label listing other pictures for sale, instead they carried a label describing the picture or portrait in detail. Such examples include: "The Forth Bridge", "Clifton Suspension Bridge", "The Lady Godiva Procession", "Ye Lady Godiva", "Sgt. Bates", "The late Fred Archer", the four boxers, and "Ye Old Crown House".

Some pictures exist which were definitely woven by Stevens but as far as is known they were never sold in mounted form with the usual Stevens' identification. Such items have not been listed as Stevengraphs in the main text but they are referred to on page 92, as are other pictures possibly made by Stevens but not seen by the author in an original mount with Stevens' identification.

## Size

There is considerable variation both in the size and shape of the silk and the mount. See under "Abbreviations" for further explanation. Care should be taken to see that the mount has not been unduly cut down to fit into a frame which was too small for it.

## Condition

The picture or portrait must be in its original cardboard mount for it to be regarded as a genuine specimen. Those silks which have been remounted are of much less value and a collector will usually prefer a Stevengraph in its original mount even if it is rather stained, discoloured or cut down.

Care should be taken to keep the pictures in good condition. They are very susceptible to damp and to fading, and should be kept away from cold, damp walls and away from direct sunlight and south facing walls.

The cardboard mounts become very brittle with age and can crack with the slightest bending, so they should be framed for safety.

## Colours

Nineteenth-century dyes fade badly which accounts for the drab appearance of many horse-racing Stevengraphs seen today. The keen collector will prefer Stevengraphs which have not faded badly and such specimens are always worth a substantial premium.

Violets, pinks, greens and blues are especially vulnerable if kept on a wall exposed to direct or even indirect sunlight. The horse-racing pictures in their original colours are most beautiful, with each jockey in his owner's bright racing colours.

Sometimes one finds a Stevengraph with an apparent colour variation but close examination will show that it is a case of colour fading. It may be possible to depress the silk very carefully and peer behind the gilding. This will usually reveal some trace of the original unfaded colours. Only consistent colour variations have been noted in the text as (a) and (b) numbers.

## Stevens' trade labels

All mounted pictures and portraits which left the factory for retail sale had a trade label stuck to the back with the exception of some late versions, certain portraits and those Stevengraphs which had a special descriptive label.

The trade label gives some indication of the age of the Stevengraph. Labels with only one subject listed on them were the earliest (1879), and those with four or five, probably about 1880–81.

Some of the later subjects can be dated approximately by reference to whether or not the label lists Queen Victoria as being *the late* Queen Victoria, while even later labels will list King George V and Queen Mary.

Many subjects never appeared on any of the labels, especially those first made after 1900 by which time fashions were changing and demand was declining.

Occasionally one finds a Stevengraph with a small size "South Farnborough Silk Weaving Co." label on the back. This firm is believed to have been one of Stevens' many selling agents.

## Values

No attempt has been made to give any indication of monetary value because prices are constantly changing. The system of stars gives an approximate indication of degrees of scarcity in original titled mounts, based upon the author's opinion. Some pictures which claim a 4 or 5 star scarcity rating may in fact realise less than a 1 star item. This is because certain Stevengraphs, though scarce, are not as popular with collectors as some of the common 1 star items, and they do not yet command the price that their scarcity should demand.

Loose or remounted silks can be much more common than ones in their original titled mounts. For example, only one copy is known of STG 137 ("View of Blackpool") in its original titled mount, but loose ribbons, probably taken from postcards, are quite common.

The portraits have always been less popular but they are likely to catch up when a few more collectors appreciate their superb delicate weaving which reproduces the facial expressions, the whiskers and wrinkles as faithfully as the camera, while the range

7

of colours amongst the portraits adds brightness to any collection.

Those pictures and portraits which are most commonly found today were those which were most popular 80 to 90 years ago indicating that they were sold in large numbers. Those which are very scarce today (5, 6 and 7 star items) were, no doubt, unpopular when manufactured and few were sold.

### The Photographs

A photograph of almost all subjects is included in the book. This has made unnecessary a detailed description of each item in the main text. In most cases when the photograph was thought to be adequate no further description has been given in the interests of keeping this book as compact as possible.

### Titles

There are differences in the style of the lettering of the titles, according to the period of manufacture. Certain subjects are occasionally found with German and French titles either in addition to or in place of the English title.

### Restoration Advice

If the mount is the original, but is dirty, stained or discoloured, gentle attention with a clean soft India rubber may remove some of the marks. Gentle rubbing with new white bread may help to remove dirt from the actual silk but great care should be taken to see that the silk does not split.

The mounts are very brittle, and if cracked or broken nothing can really be done to repair the damage. The best solution is to have a new mount cut with the same external dimensions as the original, with a large enough aperture for the silkwork and the title. Similarly if the mount is badly cut down, the appearance of the picture can be restored by having a new mount cut with the correct external dimensions, with an aperture slightly larger than the silkwork and the title. Place the new mount over the old mount and frame the whole thing.

On no account should a mount be placed in water or against steam in an attempt to remove stains. The mount will swell and distort and become water stained, while the colours of the silk may run everywhere!

## Stevens' Competitors

Stevens' principal competitor was the firm of W. H. Grant of Foleshill, Coventry, although Stevens had a lead of many years.

In quality, variety of subject and popularity, Grant's products could not have been a match for Stevens. Grant produced only a limited variety of portraits and pictures, and the fact that his products are today scarcer than Stevens' suggests that far fewer were sold because popularity for these novelties had probably begun to decline by the time that Grant had perfected the technique.

Care should be taken not to purchase a Grant military or royalty portrait in mistake for a Stevens of the same subject, because some of Grant's bore no name as was the case with Stevens'.

The following are some of the subjects made by Grant in approximate "Stevengraph" sizes:

Stage coach scene; Views of London streets and buildings; Views of Edinburgh streets and buildings; Ocean liner entitled "'Gainst Wind and Wave"; River scene entitled "'Gainst Wind and Stream"; "The Statue of Liberty in New York Harbour"; "The old Tyne bridge, Newcastle upon Tyne"; "Newcastle Exhibition, Newcastle upon Tyne"; Various pictures depicting Shakespearean property; "Kenilworth Castle"; "Britannia with emblems"; "Beaconsfield"; "Gladstone"; "Salisbury"; "Churchill"; "Beecher"; "Queen Victoria" (3 different ones); "King Edward VII"; "Queen Alexandra"; "King George V and Queen Mary"; "The Duke and Duchess of Cornwall & York"; "The Prince and Princess of Wales"; "Sir Walter Scott"; "Bright"; "Joseph Arch"; "Shakespeare"; "Kitchener;" "Buller"; "Baden Powell"; "General French"; "Roberts"; "General White"; "Lambton".

Some portraits were made both with and without a spray of flowers underneath.

Many additional subjects were made in postcard size. These can be identified as Grants' because he used a printed decorative surround to the silk, whereas on Stevens' postcards there is an embossed decorative surround.

B

9

## Abbreviations

The words in the text appearing in inverted commas indicate the title of the subject, either printed on the mount or woven into the silk.

LV = A late version exists, usually in dark mount and no back label, often without any title. Sometimes with "woven in silk by Thomas Stevens (Coventry) Ltd" printed in very small letters on the front.

\* = Common, extending to \*\*\*\*\*\*\* = very rare.

PC = Also exists in postcard form, usually with the silkwork reduced in size.

TP = Title printed on mount.

TW = Title woven into the silk.

WS = Signature woven into the silk below the portrait.

NS = No signature woven in. Applicable only to jockeys.

DBL = Descriptive back label, either a label describing the construction, history, or other information about the subject, or, in the case of portraits, a label describing the person's achievements.

G = Often found in pale green mount with no printed title and no trade label, just "woven in pure silk" printed on the front.

## External Dimensions of Mount (width dimensions given first)

SZ 1 = approximately $8'' \times 5''$; silk picture proportionately smaller

SZ 2 =     ,,     $7'' \times 5\frac{1}{4}''$; ,,     ,,       ,,       ,,

SZ 3 =     ,,     $9\frac{1}{2}'' \times 6\frac{1}{2}''$; ,,     ,,       ,,       ,,

SZ 4 =     ,,     $11'' \times 7''$; ,,     ,,       ,,       ,,

SZ P = Standard portrait size, $5\frac{1}{2}'' \times 7\frac{1}{4}''$; silk picture proportionately smaller.

Usual calendar size, $9'' \times 12''$; silk picture proportionately smaller.

# PART I

## SECTION 1. PORTRAITS

1. British Royalty portraits
2. Jockey portraits
3. Military portraits
4. Politicians
5. Notables and Sportsmen
6. Religious, Classical and Historical portraits
7. American portraits
8. Foreign Royalty portraits

**STG 1**

11

STG 2

STG 3

Her Majesty Queen Victoria

Her Majesty Queen Victoria

STG 4

STG 5

# 1. BRITISH ROYALTY PORTRAITS

Queen Victoria; The Princess of Wales, later Queen Alexandra; The Prince of Wales, later King Edward VII; The Duchess of Cornwall & York, The Princess of Wales, later Queen Mary; The Duke of Cornwall and York, The Prince of Wales, later King George V; Queen Elizabeth and King George VI.

## Queen Victoria

*STG 1*    "Queen Victoria and Her Premiers." Central portrait of the Queen facing left, surrounded by portraits of nine Premiers; views of Balmoral, Houses of Parliament and Windsor underneath.
SZ 7" × 9"    TP            \*\*\*\*\*

*STG 2*    "Her Majesty Queen Victoria. Queen of an Empire on which the sun never sets." Portrait facing left.
SZ P    TW    PC    G            \*

*STG 3*    "Her Majesty Queen Victoria. 1837 Jubilee 1887." Portrait facing right.
SZ P    TW    G            \*

*STG 4*    "Queen Victoria, born May 24th, 1819, crowned June 28th, 1838." Portrait facing right.
SZ P    TW            \*\*\*\*\*\*

*STG 5*    "Her Majesty the late Queen Victoria" woven in red at the bottom of the picture. "Born May 24th 1819. Died Jan. 22nd 1901" woven in blue below the portrait, and views of Osborne and Windsor woven underneath. Portrait facing left.
SZ P    G            \*\*\*\*\*

*STG 5a*    The same portrait, except that the title "Her Majesty the late Queen Victoria" is woven in blue, the same colour as her sash.
SZ P    G            \*\*\*\*\*

13

WOVEN IN PURE SILK BY T. STEVENS, COVENTRY.

H.R.H. Princess of Wales.

STG 6

WOVEN IN PURE SILK BY T. STEVENS, COVENTRY.

H.R.H. Princess of Wales

STG 7

HER MAJESTY
QUEEN ALEXANDRA

STG 8

**The Princess of Wales—later Queen Alexandra**

*STG 6* "H.R.H. Princess of Wales." Portrait facing right above the flag. (The pair to STG 10.)
SZ P     TP                        \*\*\*\*\*\*\*

*STG 7* "H.R.H. Princess of Wales." Portrait facing half right, with golden string of beads and mauve dress. No flag. (The pair to STG 11.)
SZ P     TP                         \*\*\*\*\*\*

*STG 8* "Her Majesty Queen Alexandra." Crests of England, Scotland and Ireland appear below the portrait. Regd. No. 372130 usually woven in. No flag.
SZ P     TW     G     PC                 \*

WOVEN IN PURE SILK BY T. STEVENS, COVENTRY.

H.R.H. Prince of Wales.

WOVEN IN PURE SILK BY T. STEVENS, COVENTRY.

H.R.H. Prince of Wales.

STG 10                                      STG 11

STG 12

## The Prince of Wales, later King Edward VII

*STG 9* "H.R.H. The Prince of Wales." Portrait facing ahead with the flags below.

SZ P    TP                            *******

*STG 10* "H.R.H. The Prince of Wales." Portrait facing left with the flags below. A later version of STG 9.

SZ P    TP                            *******

*STG 11* "H.R.H. Prince of Wales." A later portrait facing left with scarlet tunic and golden sash. No flag.

SZ P    TP                            *****

*STG 12* "His Majesty King Edward VII." Below the portrait is the royal coat of arms and views of Windsor and Parliament. No flag. The pair to STG 8.

SZ P    TW    PC    G                  *

STG 13                                                    STG 14

## The Duchess of Cornwall & York, The Princess of Wales, later Queen Mary

*STG 13* "H.R.H. The Duchess of Cornwall & York." Title woven in red. Regd. No. 373873 usually woven in green.
SZ P      TW      G                                      *****

*Note:* This portrait exists with the title completely omitted.

*STG 14* "H.R.H. Princess of Wales." Title woven in red. Regd. No. 373873 woven in. Portrait facing right, and identical to STG 13 except for the title. Pair to STG 17.
SZ P      TW      G                                      ******

*STG 15* "Her Majesty Queen Mary." The Queen is pictured with crown and coronation dress. The pair to STG 18.
SZ P      TP      PC                                     ******

17

Her Majesty Queen Mary

STG 15

**The Duke of Cornwall & York, the Prince of Wales, later King George V**

*STG 16* "H.R.H. The Duke of Cornwall & York." Title woven in black across the anchor, with crown, warships and leaves as in STG 17.

SZ P    TW    G                  *\*\*\*\*\**

*STG 17* "H.R.H. The Prince of Wales." Regd. No. 373520 usually woven in. Depicts four warships, red crown, large black anchor and deep green leaves below the portrait.

SZ P    TW    G                  *\*\*\*\*\*\**

*Note:* This portrait exists with the title completely omitted.

18

STG 16

STG 17

STG 18

*STG 18* "His Majesty King George V." The king is shown in full coronation robes.

SZ P     TP     PC  \*\*\*\*\*\*

## Queen Elizabeth and King George VI

*STG 19* "Her Majesty Queen Elizabeth." Large portrait of the Queen facing right, set in rectangular border frame of thistles and shamrocks, with two flags below, and castles and cathedrals in each corner. Usually found in calendar form dated 1937 or 1938.

SZ 9″ × 12″     TP            \*\*\*\*

STG 19                              STG 20

*STG 20* "His Majesty King George VI." Large portrait of the King facing left with similar border frame, flag and buildings to STG 19. Usually found in calendar form dated 1937 or 1938.

SZ 9″ × 12″     TP            \*\*\*

# MORE THAN SEVEN AND A HALF CENTURIES
## AFTER GODIVA

— In 1846 CASH'S began weaving pictures like this. Throughout the intervening years, the company has adapted and developed its craft to suit changing tastes and conditions. Today CASH'S have gained world-wide fame for RIBBONS, WOVEN NAME TAPES and GARMENT LABELS, as well as pictures woven with infinite care and skill.

*Statue of Lady Godiva woven by J. & J. CASH LTD. OF COVENTRY*
*in 1967 to mark that city's 900th Anniversary*

WOVEN IN PURE SILK BY T. STEVENS, COVENTRY.

THE LATE

FRED. ARCHER.

STG 23

WOVEN IN PURE SILK BY T. STEVENS, COVENTRY.

F. BARRATT.

STG 30

WOVEN IN PURE SILK BY T. STEVENS, COVENTRY.

TOM CANNON.

STG 31

## 2. JOCKEY PORTRAITS

Archer; Barratt; Cannon; Osborne; Wood.

### Archer

"The late Fred Archer."  SZ P  TP  DBL

| STG | Owner's Name | | Colour of Body | Sleeves | Cap | DBL |
|---|---|---|---|---|---|---|
| 21 | Lord Falmouth | NS WS | Black | White | Red | * |
| 22 | Mr Manton[1] | NS WS | Scarlet | Scarlet | Scarlet | ** |
| 23 | Duke of Westminster | NS WS | Primrose | Primrose | Black | *** |
| 24 | Mr Peck[2] | WS | Blue | Orange | Blue | ** |
| 25 | Mr T. Jennings[3] | WS | Silver grey | Silver grey | Black | ***** |
| 26 | ?[3] | WS | Silver grey | Primrose | Silver grey | ****** |
| 27 | Prince of Wales | WS | Blue | Scarlet | Black | * |
| 28 | Mr Dover[2] | NS | Blue | Orange | Black | ***** |
| 29 | ? | NS | White | Primrose | Black | ****** |

*Notes*
[1] "Mr Manton" was a pseudonym for the Duchess of Montrose, women not being allowed to run horses.

[2] Stevens' back label gives Mr Peck's colours as incorporating a black cap. This must have been a mistake because Ruff's *Guide to Turf* 1880 gives the registered colours of Mr Peck as incorporating a blue cap and the registered colours of Mr Dover as incorporating the black cap.

[3] According to Ruff's *Guide to Turf*, Mr T. Jennings, jr's, colours were French grey (silver grey) body and sleeves, black cap. STG 26 has, however, been seen with "T. Jennings jr." stamped in violet on the back, so this must have been another error in the factory.

23

## Barratt

"F. Barratt"   SZ P   TP

| STG | Owner's Name | | Colour of Body | Sleeves | Cap | |
|---|---|---|---|---|---|---|
| 30 | Mr R. Martin | NS | White | Black | Black | **** |

## Cannon

"Tom Cannon"   SZ P   TP

| STG | Owner's Name | | Colour of Body | Sleeves | Cap | |
|---|---|---|---|---|---|---|
| 31 | His own colours | NS WS | White and Scarlet hoops | | White | * |
| 32 | Lord Roseberry | NS WS | Rose and Primrose hoops | | Rose | * |
| 33 | Baron de Rothschild | WS | Blue and Yellow hoops | | Yellow | ***** |
| 34 | H. Crocker | WS | Blue | Blue | Gold | *** |

*Note:* STG 32 often appears as pink and cream on account of the rose and primrose having faded badly.

STG 32 is sometimes found with horizontal stripes as opposed to hoops.

## Osborne

"John Osborne"   SZ P   TP

| STG | Owner's Name | | Colour of Body | Sleeves | Cap | |
|---|---|---|---|---|---|---|
| 35 | Prince Soltykoff | NS | Deep Rose with Black sash | Deep Rose | Deep Rose | ** |
| 36 | Sir Green Price oi Mr R. C. Vyners | NS | Violet with White sash | Violet | Violet | *** |

24

JOHN OSBORNE.

STG 36

C. WOOD.

STG 37

## Wood

"C. Wood"  SZ P  TP

| STG | Owner's Name | | Colour of Body | Sleeves | Cap | |
|-----|--------------|-----|------|---------|-----|---|
| 37 | Mr Peck | WS | Blue | Orange | Blue | *** |
|  |  | NS |  |  |  |  |
| 38 | Capt. Christie or Gen. Wood | NS | Cream | Cream | Cream | ****** |
| 39 | ? | WS | Yellow | Silvery Blue | Silvery Blue | ***** |
|  |  | NS |  |  |  |  |

c

25

WOVEN IN PURE SILK BY T. STEVENS, COVENTRY.

**STG 40**

WOVEN IN PURE SILK BY T. STEVENS, COVENTRY.

**STG 41**

WOVEN IN PURE SILK.

**STG 42**

WOVEN IN SILK BY T. STEVENS (COVENTRY) LTD.

**STG 43**

## 3. MILITARY PORTRAITS

†Baden Powell; †Buller; †French; A Gentleman in Kharki; †Kitchener; Macdonald; †Roberts; Wauchope.

### Baden Powell

**STG 40**   "Baden Powell". 'Prince of Scouts and Hero of Mafeking' is woven in blue within red sash. Regd. No. 355916 woven in lower left.

SZ P        TW        G                                                    **

### Buller

**STG 41**   "Buller." Title sometimes not woven in, thus giving the portrait no title at all. "Tucela Relief of Ladysmith Feb. 28th 1900" woven in red.

SZ P        TW        G                                                    *

### French

**STG 42**   "Maj. Gen. J. P. D. French." Portrait facing left.
SZ P        TW        G                                                    ****

**STG 43**   "Field Marshal Sir John French." Quite a different portrait to STG 42.
SZ P        TW                                                        *******

### Gentleman in Kharki

**STG 44**   "A Gentleman in Kharki. R. Coton Woodville 1899." The picture is copied from a painting by Mr Coton Woodville. The back label states "This pure silk woven picture of 'A Gentleman in Kharki' (by Mr R. Coton Woodville) is produced by permission of the 'London Daily Mail' and part proceeds of sale go to the 'Daily Mail Fund'."

SZ P        TW        PC                                              *****

### Kitchener

**STG 45**   "Kitchener of Khartoum." Regd. No. 355800 also woven in red.
SZ P        TW        G        PC                                         *

---

† Grant also produced these subjects without his name on.

27

STG 44

STG 45

STG 47

STG 48

## Macdonald

*STG 46* "Maj.-Gen. H. A. Macdonald, C.B., D.S.O." Portrait facing left.

SZ P    TW    G                                    *****

*STG 47* "Maj.-Gen. H. A. Macdonald, C.B., D.S.O." Portrait facing right.

SZ P    TW    G                                    *****

*STG 48* "Maj.-Gen. Sir H. A. Macdonald, C.B., D.S.O." Portrait facing left. (This portrait is identical to STG 46 but the title is in more vertical lettering to enable the word "Sir" to be fitted in.)

SZ P    TW    G                                    *******

## Roberts

*STG 49* "Roberts, F. M." Signature woven across the base, or sometimes in smaller writing half across the base. Variations exist in the position of the leaves and the flag. Regd. No. 350091 often woven in.

SZ P    G                                          *

## Wauchope

*STG 50* "Maj.-Gen. Wauchope, C.B. (killed in Action)."

SZ P    TW    G                                    *****

STG 49

STG 50

The late Earl of Beaconsfield

STG 52

STG 53

THE LATE

Rt. Hon. John Bright, M.P.

BORN NOV. 16, 1811.   DIED MARCH 27, 1889.

STG 56

Rt. Hon. J. Chamberlain, M.P

STG 58

## 4. POLITICIANS

Beaconsfield; Bright; Chamberlain; Churchill; Gladstone; Parnell; Salisbury.

### Beaconsfield

*STG 51*    "The late Earl of Beaconsfield." Black and white portrait facing left. No primroses.
SZ P     TP                                    **

*STG 52*    "The late Earl of Beaconsfield." Similar to STG 51 but there is a spray of primroses below the portrait.
SZ P     TP                                    *

*STG 53*    "The late Earl of Beaconsfield." Title woven in colours above the portrait. This silk is only $1\frac{5}{8}'' \times 3\frac{1}{4}''$; mount $4\frac{1}{2}'' \times 6''$.          *****

### Bright

*STG 54*    "Rt. Hon. John Bright, M.P." Black and white portrait without flowers.
SZ P     TP                              *****

*STG 55*    "Rt. Hon. John Bright, M.P." Similar to STG 54 but with a spray of water lilies.
SZ P     TP                            ******

*STG 56*    "The late Rt. Hon. John Bright, M.P." The same portrait as STG 55 with water lilies but with different title.
SZ P     TP                              *****

### Chamberlain

*STG 57*    "Rt. Hon. J. Chamberlain, M.P." Black and white portrait facing left without flowers.
SZ P     TP                              *****

*STG 58*    "Rt. Hon. J. Chamberlain, M.P." Similar to STG 57 but with a spray of orchids.
SZ P     TP                            ****

WOVEN IN PURE SILK BY T. STEVENS, COVENTRY.

Rt. Hon. Lord R. Churchill, M.P.

**STG 60**

WOVEN IN PURE SILK BY T. STEVENS, COVENTRY.

Rt. Hon. W. E. Gladstone, M.P.

**STG 63**

WOVEN IN PURE SILK BY T. STEVENS, COVENTRY.

Rt. Hon. W. E. Gladstone, M.P.

**STG 64**

## Churchill

**STG 59** "Rt. Hon. Lord R. Churchill, M.P." Black and white portrait without flowers.
SZ P    TP    \*\*\*\*\*

**STG 60** "Rt. Hon. Lord R. Churchill, M.P." Similar to STG 59 but with a spray of flowers.
SZ P    TP    \*\*\*\*\*

**STG 61** "The late Lord R. Churchill, M.P." Similar to STG 60 except for the different title.
SZ P    TP    \*\*\*\*\*\*

## Gladstone

**STG 62** "Rt. Hon. W. E. Gladstone, M.P." Portrait facing right. No flowers.
SZ P    TP    \*\*

**STG 63** "Rt. Hon. W. E. Gladstone, M.P." Portrait looking ahead with spray of thistles and roses.
SZ P    TP    \*

*Note:* Variations exist in the shape of the roses and their colour as distinct from colour fading which is common.

**STG 64** "Rt. Hon. W. E. Gladstone, M.P." Portrait facing right with spray of thistles and roses.
SZ P    TP    \*\*\*

**STG 65** "Rt. Hon. W. E. Gladstone, M.P." The same portrait as STG 64, facing right, but with a very much smaller head. The measurement from base of collar to top of hair is 2.3″ against 2.6″ on STG 64.
SZ P    TP    \*\*\*\*\*\*

**STG 66** "Rt. Hon. W. E. Gladstone, M.P." Title woven in green, red and violet above the portrait which faces right. Spray of flowers at the foot, the pair to STG 53.
Silk size $1\frac{5}{8}″ \times 3\frac{1}{4}″$ in a mount $4\frac{1}{2}″ \times 6″$    \*\*\*\*\*

**STG 67** "The late Rt. Hon. W. E. Gladstone, M.P." Exactly similar to STG 63 except for the title.
SZ P    TP    \*\*\*\*

33

Charles Stewart Parnell, M.P.

STG 69

Marquis of Salisbury. K.G.

STG 72

## Parnell

*STG 68*  "Charles Stewart Parnell, M.P." Nothing woven below the portrait.

SZ P    TP                      \*\*\*\*\*\*

*STG 69*  "Charles Stewart Parnell, M.P." Clover leaves, red bow and yellow harp woven below the portrait.

SZ P    TP                       \*\*\*\*

*STG 70*  "The late Charles Stewart Parnell, M.P." Exactly similar to STG 69 except for the title.

SZ P    TP                       \*\*\*\*\*\*

> It cannot be emphasised too often that the stars signifying degrees of scarcity only refer to specimens in their original titled mounts, and not to loose ribbons or remounted items.

**Salisbury**

***STG 71*** "Marquis of Salisbury, K.G." No flowers.

SZ P  TP        \*\*\*\*

***STG 72*** "Marquis of Salisbury, K.G." Spray of red roses below the portrait.

SZ P  TP        \*\*\*

***STG 72a*** Similar to STG 72 except that the roses are bright yellow and orange.

SZ P  TP        \*\*\*\*\*

---

35

## 5. NOTABLES AND SPORTSMEN

Burns; W. G. Grace; Howell; Shakespeare; Stanley; Stephenson; Kilrain; Mitchell; Smith; Sullivan; Sandell Stevens.

### Burns

**STG 73**  "Burns." Four lines of verse in green, and the title "Burns" in black, are woven above the portrait, which faces right. The portrait is much smaller than STG 74, and apart from small details it is similar to a bookmarker depicting the poet. Below the portrait is a spray of thistles.
Silk size 2″ × 3¾″.   SZP   *******

**STG 74**  "Robert Burns." Portrait facing right with spray of thistles below. A later version than STG 73.
SZ P   TP   *****

STG 73

STG 74

WOVEN IN PURE SILK BY T. STEVENS, COVENTRY.

R. HOWELL,

CHAMPION OF THE WORLD.

STG 75

STG 76

## W. G. Grace

*STG 75* "W.G." This is the only title. A full length picture of the famous cricketer at the wicket, on the occasion of his century of centuries.

SZ P     TP          ******

## Howell

*STG 76* "R. Howell, Champion of the World." The portrait is set above a penny farthing race.

SZ P     TP          *******

# SHAKESPEARE

AND VIEWS OF STRATFORD.

STG 77

# H. M. STANLEY.

STG 78

George Stephenson,

THE PIONEER OF RAILWAYS.

STG 79

## Shakespeare

*STG 77* "Shakespeare and Views of Stratford." Above the portrait are views of "Shakespeare's Birthplace" and "Anne Hathaway's Cottage", while below are views of "Stratford Church" and "Shakespeare Memorial".

SZ P    TP             \*\*\*\*\*\*\*

## Stanley

*STG 78* "H. M. Stanley." The famous explorer.

SZ P    TP             \*\*\*\*\*\*\*

## Stephenson

*STG 79* "George Stephenson, the Pioneer of Railways" or "George Stephenson". Above the portrait is the word "Past" woven in red with pictures of the "First Locomotive" and "The Rocket". Below is a modern train with "Present" woven in red. Regd. No. 72397 printed twice on the front of the mount.

SZ P    TP    PC          \*\*\*\*\*\*

JAKE KILRAIN.          C. MITCHELL.

JEM SMITH.          JOHN L. SULLIVAN.

**Kilrain**

*STG 80*  "Jake Kilrain." Full length picture of the American boxing champion. The belt is red, white and blue.

SZ P     TP     DBL              ****

**Mitchell**

*STG 81*  "C. Mitchell." The British pugilist. The socks are red.

SZ P     TP     DBL              ****

**Smith**

*STG 82*  "Jem Smith." The British pugilist. His belt is red, white and blue. The socks are found in either green, yellow, or black.

SZ P     TP     DBL              ***

**Sullivan**

*STG 83*  "John L. Sullivan." The American pugilist. Red, white and blue belt. The socks are found in white or red.

SZ P     TP     DBL              ***

*Note:* On superb unfaded copies of the four boxers, the exposed parts of the body are in pink.

**Sandell Stevens**

*STG 84*   "Sandell Stevens." Title woven in. A black and white portrait of Thomas Stevens' grandson. This has only been seen in a mount with two apertures, and in post-card form. In the left aperture is the portrait and in the right one a picture of a terrier, seated, with the title "Prince" woven in. The portrait was apparently pro-duced just for members of the family and very few specimens are known. It is one of the rarest Steven-graphs.
SZ  10″ × 7½″    PC                        *******

42

43

## 6. RELIGIOUS, CLASSICAL AND HISTORICAL PORTRAITS

Ecce Homo; Immaculate; Leda; Madonna and Child; Mater Dolorosa; Peeping Tom; Psyche.

### Ecce Homo

*STG 85*   "Ecce Homo." Picture of Christ with crown of thorns, with a red cloak over His shoulders.

SZ P   TP   PC                                    ******

### Immaculate

*STG 86*   "The Immaculate." Full length picture of the Virgin Mary with arms outstretched.

SZ P   TP                                     *******

STG 85

STG 86

**Madonna**

*STG 87* "Madonna and Child." Against a gold and yellow background the Madonna is pictured in brilliant red, blue and golden garments.

SZ P    TP    PC                     \*\*\*\*\*\*\*

STG 88

**Mater Dolorosa**

*STG 88* "Mater Dolorosa." Title printed on mount and woven in red. The picture is in black, white, red and gold.

SZ P    PC                        \*\*\*\*\*\*

45

WOVEN IN SILK BY THOMAS STEVENS (COVENTRY) LTD.

Peeping Tom

LEDA.

STG 89

STG 91

WOVEN IN PURE SILK BY T. STEVENS, COVENTRY, ENG.

SERGT. G. H. BATES,
THE AMERICAN STANDARD BEARER.

STG 92

**Peeping Tom**

*STG 89*   "Peeping Tom." Title printed, with "Ye Peeping Tom of Coventre" woven in. The picture is in brilliant red, green, blue and yellow with grey and brown window surround.
SZ P    PC                                    ★★★★

**Psyche**

*STG 90*   "The Bath of Psyche." The title and "woven in silk" are printed in gold. Full length picture of Psyche undressing at the bath with reflections of her feet in the blue water. Mount usually dark green without gilding and no trade label.
SZ 8½" × 14½"                              ★★★★★★

**Leda**

*STG 91*   "Leda." A superb study of Leda and the Swan, believed to have been manufactured for the French market.
SZ 7½" × 9"    TP    ★★★★★★★

STG 90

47

WOVEN IN PURE SILK BY T. STEVENS, COVENTRY, ENG.

# BUFFALO BILL.
(COL. W. F. CODY.)

STG 93

# W. F. CODY,
(BUFFALO BILL.)

STG 94

WOVEN IN PURE SILK BY T. STEVENS, COVENTRY

# PRES<sup>DT.</sup> CLEVELAND.

STG 95

WOVEN IN PURE SILK BY T. STEVENS, COVENTRY.

# Mrs. Cleveland.
QUEEN OF 60 MILLIONS OF FREE PEOPLE.

STG 96

## 7. PORTRAITS OF FAMOUS AMERICANS

Bates; Buffalo Bill; Cleveland; Mrs Cleveland; Harrison; Washington.

### Bates

**STG 92** "Sergt. G. H. Bates, the American Standard Bearer."
SZ P    TP    DBL    WS    ******

### Buffalo Bill

**STG 93** "Buffalo Bill (Col. W. F. Cody)." Usual size portrait of the famous man.
SZ P    TP    DBL    WS    *****

**STG 94** "W. F. Cody (Buffalo Bill)." Larger version than STG 93, depicting Cody surrounded by portraits of seven Red Indian chiefs and one American.
SZ 7″ × 9″    TP    ******

**STG 94a** The same picture as STG 94 except that the title is "Souvenir of the Wild West."
SZ 7″ × 9″    TP    ******

### Cleveland

**STG 95** "Presdt. Cleveland." The back label comprises a list of U.S. Presidents and Generals, and Wars involving the U.S.A.
SZ P    TP    WS    ******

### Mrs Cleveland

**STG 96** "Mrs Cleveland (Queen of 60 millions of free people)." With a spray of violets below the portrait. The back label comprises poems entitled "America" and "The Star Spangled Banner".
SZ P    TP    ******

---

It cannot be emphasised too often that the stars signifying degrees of scarcity only refer to specimens in their original titled mounts, and not to loose ribbons or remounted items.

---

**Harrison**

*STG 97* "B. Harrison, President of the United States."

SZ P     TP     WS         ******

**Washington**

*STG 98* "George Washington."

SZ P     TP            *******

STG 97

# 8. PORTRAITS OF EUROPEAN ROYALTY AND NOTABLES
## All sz p.

*STG*  *99*  "Crown Prince of Germany."        \*\*\*\*\*\*\*

*STG*  *100*  "Empress Augusta Victoria of Germany."   \*\*\*\*\*\*\*

*STG*  *101*  "Empress Alexandra (The Czarina of Russia)."  \*\*\*\*\*\*\*

*STG*  *102*  "Nicholas II (The Czar of Russia)."     \*\*\*\*\*\*\*

*STG*  *103*  "Franz Josef (of Austria)" also "Franz Josef".  \*\*\*\*\*\*

*STG*  *104*  "General Georges Boulanger." Also PC.†   \*\*\*\*\*\*\*

*STG*  *105*  "King Albert of Saxony."       \*\*\*\*\*\*\*

*STG*  *106*  "Wilhelm I."         \*\*\*\*\*\*

*STG*  *107*  "Kaiser Wilhelm II" woven in red; also "Wilhelm II". *See picture* p. 154.    \*\*\*\*\*\*

*STG*  *108*  "Kaiser Wilhelm II von Deutschland" (a different portrait to STG 107).    \*\*\*\*\*\*

*STG*  *109*  "Friedrich III Kaiser von Deutschland" also "Frederick III". *See picture* p. 154.    \*\*\*\*\*\*

*STG*  *110*  "Prinz v. Bismarck."       \*\*\*\*\*\*\*

*STG*  *111*  "The Late Prince Bismarck."     \*\*\*\*\*\*\*

*STG*  *112*  "Leopold of Bavaria."†      \*\*\*\*\*\*\*

*STG*  *113*  "Prince Moltke."       \*\*\*\*\*\*\*

*STG*  *114*  "Princess Hermine of Schonaich-Carolath."†  \*\*\*\*\*\*\*

*STG*  *115*  "Princess Hermine of Schonaich-Carolath"† (different portrait).    \*\*\*\*\*\*\*

*STG*  *116*  "Ludwig Windthorst."†     \*\*\*\*\*\*\*

*Notes*
   (i) Titles printed unless otherwise stated. Those marked † have not been seen by the author in an original mount, but the titles would almost certainly have been printed, because the title was not woven into the picture.
   (ii) All these portraits were made by Stevens for export to the Continent. This will account for their extreme scarcity in the British Isles today.

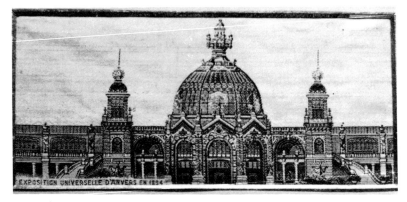

STG 117

Part I

SECTION 2. PICTURES

A. (1) Exhibitions; (2) Castles; (3) Buildings and Views; (4) Bridges

B. Historical and Classical subjects

C. (1) Horse Racing; (2) Coursing, Fox Hunting and Country activities; (3) Sports

D. (1) Boats and Ships; (2) Coaching; (3) Fire Engines; (4) Trains

WOVEN IN PURE SILK BY J. J. MANNION & CO., CINCINNATI, OHIO.

·CENTENNIAL· EXPOSITION·

OF THE OHIO VALLEY AND CENTRAL STATES.

CINCINNATI·1888

STG 118

## A. 1. EXHIBITIONS

**Antwerp Exhibition**

*STG 117* "Exposition Universelle d'Anvers."
SZ 1    TW                                    ******

**Cincinnati Exhibition**

*STG 118* "Centennial Exposition of the Ohio Valley and Central States, Cincinnati 1888." "Woven in pure silk by J. J. Mannion & Co., Cincinnati, Ohio" (Mannion is credited as one of Stevens' agents in the U.S.A. and it seems clear that some of Stevens' silks were being sold under Mannion's name. "The Finish" has been seen with similar Mannion identification.)
SZ 3    TP                                    *******

**Edinburgh Exhibition**

*STG 119* "A present from the Edinburgh International Exhibition 1886." Shows a view of the Exhibition building and four small views of Edinburgh, surmounted by the City's Coat of Arms.
SZ 10½″ × 8½″    TP                           ******

STG 119

STG 120

**Glasgow Exhibition**

*STG 120* "International Exhibition Glasgow 1888."

SZ 3      TP                                                    *****

**Manchester Exhibition**

*STG 121* "Royal Jubilee Exhibition Manchester 1887."

SZ 1      TP                                                    ******

**Newcastle Exhibition**

*STG 122* "Royal Jubilee Exhibition, Newcastle upon Tyne 1887."

SZ 2      TP                                                    *******

STG 121

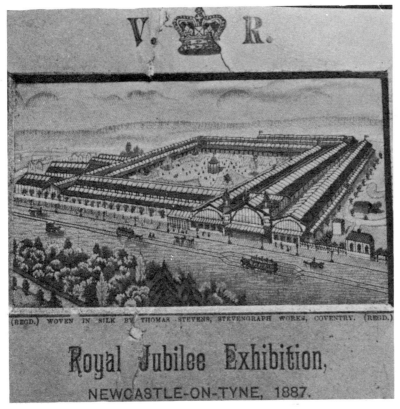

(REGD.) WOVEN IN SILK BY THOMAS STEVENS, STEVENGRAPH WORKS, COVENTRY. (REGD.)

## Royal Jubilee Exhibition,
### NEWCASTLE-ON-TYNE, 1887.

## A. 2. CASTLES

These pictures were made from about 1918 onwards, often in the form of calendars.

**STG 123** "Balmoral Castle." A colourful view of Balmoral with blue sky, green trees and grass, red flowers and flowering shrubs.

SZ 4     TP     LV         ***

STG 123

STG 124

STG 125

STG 126

STG 127

**STG 124** "Conway Castle and Bridge." Often no title. In black and white with blue sky and green trees.
sz 4    LV    *****

**STG 125** "Kenilworth Castle." Large size black and white picture. Title woven in lower right corner. Stevens' identification printed on front. No back label.
sz $19\frac{1}{2}'' \times 12\frac{1}{2}''$    TW    **

**STG 126** "Kenilworth Castle." Smaller version than STG 125. Colours black and white with blue sky and green bushes.
sz 4    LV    TP    *****

**STG 127** "Warwick Castle—The River Front."
sz 4    LV    TP    *****

**STG 128** "Windsor Castle." A colourful view of the castle with the Thames below. Often no title.
sz 4    LV    ****

## A. 3. BUILDINGS AND VIEWS

**Coventry**

*STG 129* "Coventry." Large size black and white picture depicting Grey Friar's Green in Coventry as it was in Edwardian days. Title woven in lower left corner. Stevens' identification printed on front. No back label.
*See picture* p. 154.
sz $19\frac{1}{2}" \times 12\frac{1}{2}"$   TW   PC   **\*\***

*STG 130* "Coventry Old and New." Depicts Coventry Cathedral and six other City views.
SZ P   PC   TP   **\*\*\*\*\***

STG 130

STG 132

58

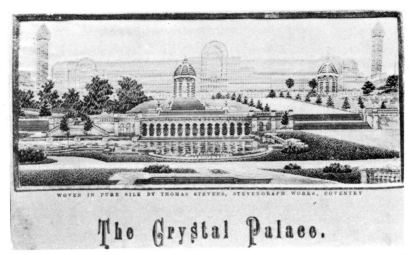

WOVEN IN PURE SILK BY THOMAS STEVENS, STEVENGRAPH WORKS, COVENTRY

The Crystal Palace.

STG 131

## Crystal Palace

*STG 131* "The Crystal Palace." The exterior view of the famous building, with green gardens and flower beds coloured red and yellow.

SZ 1    TP    **

*STG 132* "The Crystal Palace (Interior)." Interior view of the building.

SZ P    TP    *******

## Houses of Parliament

*STG 133* "Houses of Parliament." Picture in black and white with blue sky, green trees and union jack in colour. Usually no title. Often in calendar form.

SZ 4    LV    ***

STG 133

**Niagara Falls**                                             STG 134

*STG 134* "Niagara." Superb colourful view of the famous falls.
SZ 3     TW                                              ******

**Old Crown House**

*STG 135* "Ye Old Crown House." Black and white picture of the
old Tudor building in Birmingham.
SZ 2     TW     TP     DBL                               ***

STG 135

60

### Tower of London

*STG 136* "Tower of London and Tower Bridge." Colourful picture of the famous landmark in black and white, green, brown and brick red. Often no title. Sometimes in calendar form.

SZ 4    LV    ***

### View of Blackpool

*STG 137* "View of Blackpool" woven into the silk, below which is printed "A present from Blackpool" and "Woven in the Winter Gardens, Blackpool". An "aerial" view in violet of the town and piers with small boats off the beach.

SZ 2    PC    ******

*Note:* Loose unmounted silks of this subject have been seen in blue, and black and white.

VIEW OF BLACKPOOL

WOVEN IN PURE SILK BY THOMAS STEVENS, STEVENGRAPH WORKS, COVENTRY.

A Present from Blackpool.

STG 137

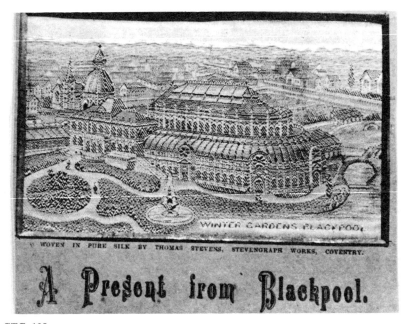

STG 138

STG 139

## Winter Gardens Blackpool

*STG 138* "Winter Gardens Blackpool" woven into the silk, below which is printed "A Present from Blackpool" and "Woven in the Winter Gardens Blackpool". The picture shows the Winter Gardens building and part of the town. The picture is found in sea-green colour throughout, and in red, and black and white.

    SZ 2    PC             *******

## Warwickshire

*STG 139* "Warwickshire Old and New." Depicts Kenilworth Castle with coloured Warwickshire views above and below.

    SZ P    TP             ******


## A. 4. BRIDGES

### Clifton Bridge

*STG 140* "Clifton Suspension Bridge." View of the bridge as completed in 1864.

    SZ 4    TP    DBL       *****

STG 140

**Forth Bridge**

*STG 141* "The Forth Bridge." The bridge is pictured under construction, in black or dark brown and white.

SZ 3    TP    DBL                                ****

*STG 142* "The Forth Bridge." The bridge is pictured in its completed state, in black or dark brown and white.

SZ 3    TP    DBL                                *****

*STG 143* "The Forth Bridge." Often no title, and in calendar form. The bridge is complete, in black and white with blue sky and distant green shoreline.

SZ 4    LV                                ******

**Old Tyne Bridge**

*STG 144* "The Old Tyne Bridge." "Regd. No. 72396." View of the early bridge over the Tyne at Newcastle.

SZ P    TP    *******

STG 144

## B. HISTORICAL AND CLASSICAL SUBJECTS

STG 145

Columbus Leaving Spain; Columbus Landing; Declaration of Independence; Dick Turpin; Lady Godiva; Nelson; Phoebus and Aurora; Radetzky; Wellington and Blucher; William of Orange.

### Columbus

***STG 145*** "Columbus Leaving Spain." Title woven in and usually also printed on mount. Sometimes found with additional identification printed on the mount "Woven in pure silk at the World's Columbian Exposition Chicago 1893".

sz 3     LV                                    *****

***STG 146*** "Landing of Columbus October 12th 1492." Title woven in and usually also printed on mount, sometimes with the same Chicago Exposition identification as STG 145.

sz 3     LV                                    ****

STG 146

**Signing of the Declaration of Independence.**

JULY 4TH, 1776.

**STG 147**

DICK TURPIN'S RIDE TO YORK.

ON HIS BONNIE BLACK BESS

1739.

Right onward she went till she staggered and dropped,
But her limbs only failed when her heart pulse had stopped;
May the steed that comes nigh her in courage and fire ;
Carry rider more worthy to make her heart tire ;
Though she saved him, and died to prove what she could do,
Yet *her* life was most precious by far of the two.

ELIZA COOK.

**STG 148**

WOVEN IN PURE SILK BY T. STEVENS, COVENTRY.

**The Lady Godiva Procession.**

**STG 150**

## Independence

***STG 147*** "Declaration of Independence July 4th 1776" woven into the silk. Often the additional title "The Signing of the Declaration of Independence July 4th 1776" is printed on the mount, sometimes with the same Chicago Exposition identification as STG 145.
SZ 3    LV                                                    *****

*Note:* The picture is almost certainly copied from a painting by Turnbull in The Capitol, Washington, showing the presentation of the Declaration of Independence to the Congress of the American Colonies at the Pennsylvanian State House.

## Dick Turpin

***STG 148*** "Dick Turpin's ride to York on his bonnie Black Bess 1739" printed on upper part of mount. Below is printed a poem by Eliza Cook, and "Woven in the York Exhibition" is often printed in lower left corner. This was one of the first four Stevengraphs manufactured at the York Exhibition in 1879.
SZ 1    TP                                                    ***

***STG 149*** "Dick Turpin's last ride on his bonnie Black Bess." This is a later version than STG 148 and has no other printed title. Exists in various widths.
SZ 1    TP                                                    **

## Lady Godiva

***STG 150*** "The Lady Godiva Procession." Variations in width.
SZ 1    TP    DBL    PC                                       *

***STG 151*** "Ye Ladye Godiva." Below the title the following lines are printed "Then she rode forth, clothed on with chastity. . . . She took the tax away, and built herself an everlasting name. Tennyson."
SZ 2    TP    PC    DBL                                       ***

*Note:* Peeping Tom is sometimes omitted from the window in upper right corner.

WOVEN IN PURE SILK.

## Ye Ladye Godiva.

Then she rode forth, clothed on with chastity.

⁂ ⁂ ⁂ ⁂ ⁂ ⁂ ⁂ ⁂ ⁂ ⁂ ⁂

She took the tax away and built herself an
everlasting name.

TENNYSON.

STG 151

THE DEATH OF NELSON.

STG 152

WOVEN IN PURE SILK BY THOMAS STEVENS, STEVENGRAPH WORKS, COVENTRY.

# PHŒBUS & AURORA.

STG 153

### Death of Nelson

*STG 152* "The Death of Nelson." A rather confused scene on the deck of The Victory at Trafalgar.

SZ 3    TP    *

### Phoebus

*STG 153* "Phoebus and Aurora." A classical scene undoubtedly copied from a painting. Title printed (sometimes partly in colour). Copies have been seen with "Designed by Owen Bros" printed below the silk. Sometimes there is no Stevens' identification printed on the mount.

SZ 3    TP    ******

### Radetzky

*STG 154* "Radetzky and King Victor Emmanuel meeting after the battle of Novara." *See picture* p. 153.

SZ 3    TP    *******

69

**STG 155**

## Wellington

***STG 155*** "Wellington and Blucher meeting after the Battle of Waterloo."

SZ 3    TP    LV                                            *

*Note:* STG 152 and 155 were probably copied from the paintings by Maclise hanging in the House of Lords, at Westminster.

## William of Orange

***STG 156*** "William of Orange crossing the Boyne." A similar style of picture to "The Death of Nelson", and "Wellington and Blucher", but much scarcer.

SZ 3    TP    LV                                        *****

**STG 156**

STG 157

## C. 1. HORSE RACING

The Start; The Water Jump; The Struggle; The Finish; Iroquois.

### The Start

*STG 157* "The Start." A flat racing scene. The silk is found in several sizes, likewise the mount, but the usual version is SZ 1. TP. LV. Sometimes found in calendar form.   *

### The Water Jump

*STG 158* "The Water Jump." A steeplechase scene with the spires of Coventry in the distance.

SZ 1     TP                                               ***

STG 158

71

**STG 160**

## The Struggle and the Finish

**STG 159** "The Struggle." This was one of the first Stevengraphs, having been woven in the York Exhibition of 1879, as is occasionally stated in print in the lower left corner of the mount or on the special York Exhibition back label.

sz 1    TP                                                                    *

**STG 160** "The Finish." This is the same silk as "The Struggle", and superseded it soon after 1879 when "The Finish" was considered a more appropriate title.

sz 1    TP                                                                    *

*Note:* Fine specimens of these racing pictures show each jockey in his owner's different colours, violets, pinks, blues, greens, yellows, reds. They are very scarce in such fine original colours.

**STG 162**

72

## Iroquois

"Iroquois, winner of the Derby 1881, owned by P. Lorillard, Esq., ridden by F. Archer." A fine picture in full colours, blue sky, green grass and deep chestnut horse.

Mount $13\frac{1}{2}'' \times 10''$; silk $8\frac{1}{2}'' \times 3\frac{3}{4}''$    TP

It is found with Archer in two different racing colours:

**STG 161** Red body; black-and-white sleeves; white cap    ******

**STG 162** Red body; red-and-black sleeves; black cap    ******
Usually found without any Stevens' identification but has been seen with the name 'Stevens' impressed on the mount.

*Note:* The picture is believed to have been made for advertising purposes to publicise the "Iroquois" brand of tobacco.

## C. 2. COURSING, FOX HUNTING AND COUNTRY ACTIVITIES

The Slip; The First Point; The Meet; Full Cry; The Death; God Speed the Plough.

## COURSING

### The Slip

**STG 163** "The Slip." The first coursing picture showing two dogs having just been released by the slipper, while the judge, mounted, is about to set off to award the first point to whichever dog follows the hare's track more accurately.
SZ 1    TP    ***

WOVEN IN SILK BY THOMAS STEVENS, INVENTOR AND MANUFACTURER, COVENTRY AND LONDON. (REGISTERED.

The Slip.

F

WOVEN IN SILK BY THOMAS STEVENS, INVENTOR AND MANUFACTURER, COVENTRY AND LONDON, (REGISTERED.)

The First Point.

**STG 164**

WOVEN IN SILK BY THOMAS STEVENS, INVENTOR AND MANUFACTURER, COVENTRY AND LONDON, (REGISTERED)

The Meet.

**STG 165**

WOVEN IN SILK BY THOMAS STEVENS, INVENTOR AND MANUFACTURER, COVENTRY AND LONDON, (REGISTERED)

Full Cry.

**STG 166**

**The First Point**

*STG 164* "The First Point." This is the pair to "The Slip" and shows the judge, who follows the dogs, awarding the first point. The slipper is shown in red standing beside the beaters.

SZ 1    TP                                                    *

*STG 164a* The same picture as STG 164 except that the slipper is not woven in.

SZ 1    TP                                                    *

## FOX HUNTING

**The Meet**

*STG 165* "The Meet." Depicts the huntsmen and hounds meeting before the hunt.

SZ 1    TP                                                    *

**Full Cry**

*STG 166* "Full Cry." The huntsmen and hounds are shown in hot pursuit of the fox.

SZ 1    TP                                                    *

**The Death**

*STG 167* "The Death." The hunt is over. This picture was evidently not as popular as "The Meet" and "Full Cry" when it was manufactured because it is much less common today indicating that fewer copies were sold.

SZ 1    TP                                                    **

STG 167

STG 168

STG 169

STG 170

## COUNTRY ACTIVITIES

### God Speed the Plough

*STG 168* "God Speed the Plough." A horse-drawn ploughing scene with a church in the background and a flock of birds above the church.

sz 1     TP                                          ***

*STG 168a* A later version of STG 168 with the flock of birds not woven in.

sz 1     TP                                          ****


## C. 3. SPORTS

Are You Ready?; The Final Spurt; The Home Stretch; The First Set; The First Touch; The First Innings; The First Over; The Last Lap; Spanish Bull-fight.

### Are You Ready?

*STG 169* "Are You Ready?" The first of the Oxford and Cambridge Boat Race pair.

sz 1     TP                                          **

### The Final Spurt

*STG 170* "The Final Spurt." The pair to "Are You Ready?", though scarcer.

sz 1     TP                                          ***

*Note:* Fine unfaded specimens of both Boat Race pictures show the faces and limbs of the crews in pink, the Cambridge oars in pale blue and the Oxford oars in dark blue.

> It cannot be emphasised too often that the stars signifying degrees of scarcity only refer to specimens in their original titled mounts, and not to loose ribbons or remounted items.

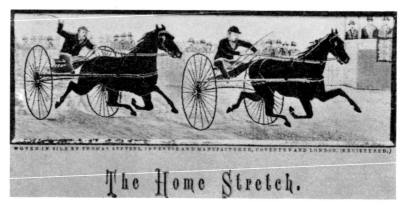

STG 171

STG 172

STG 173

**The Home Stretch**

*STG 171* "The Home Stretch." An American trotting match with two sulkies passing the judge's box. Colour variations exist in the drivers' clothing.

SZ 1    TP                                              \*\*\*\*\*

**The First Set**

*STG 172* "The First Set." A Victorian tennis match in progress, with the players and spectators in gay colours.

SZ 1    TP                                              \*\*\*\*

**The First Touch**

*STG 173* "The First Touch." A rugby match in progress with the spires of Coventry in the background.

SZ 1    TP                                              \*\*\*

**The First Innings**

*STG 174* "The First Innings." An American baseball match in progress.

SZ 1    TP                                              \*\*\*\*\*\*

STG 174

79

The First Over.

STG 175

The Last Lap.

STG 176

THE LAST LAP.

STG 177

**The First Over**

*STG 175* "The First Over." An early cricket match.

sz 1    TP                                    ****

**The Last Lap**

*STG 176* "The Last Lap." A penny-farthing race with a large line of spectators in the background. The axles, shafts and saddles are in black.

sz 1    TP                                    **

*STG 176a* The same picture, except that the axle shafts and saddles are in golden yellow and the riders' clothing is in different colours to STG 176.

sz 1    TP                                    **

*STG 177* "The Last Lap." A modern bicycle race with flags flying from the grandstand. This picture is very rare and was, therefore, obviously not a best seller when manufactured.

sz 1    TP                                    *******

**Spanish Bullfight**

*STG 178* "Spanish Bullfight." A colourful picture depicting a packed arena, the bull, matadors and a picador.

sz 1    TP    PC                              *****

WOVEN IN SILK

Spanish Bullfight

STG 178

81

# Called to the Rescue

### Heroism at Sea.

## D. 1. BOATS AND SHIPS

Called to the Rescue; Grace Darling; Battleships.

### Called to the Rescue

*STG 179* "Called to the Rescue. Heroism at Sea." A blue life-boat is shown in a stormy sea going to the assistance of a sinking sailing ship. "Heroism at Sea" is sometimes omitted, and inconsistent varieties of colour exist in the crew's clothing.

SZ 1      TP                                                    *

### Grace Darling

*STG 180* "Grace Darling." The lighthouse keeper's daughter rowing in rough seas. Blue neck piece and skirts with red blouse.

SZ 1      TP      LV                                  ****

*Grace Darling.*

***STG 180a*** The same as STG 180 except that the colours are quite different: green neck piece and skirts with mauve blouse.

SZ 1 TP LV **\*\*\*\***

## Battleships

Certain back labels list "Battleship", which covers all the following ships. STG 181 to 184*a* are basically similar, depicting a late 19th-century, two-funnelled gunboat with red-coated marines and blue-coated sailors on the deck. The sea is bright blue, and the flags are red, white and blue.

***STG 181*** "H.M.S. Hannibal." Title woven below the bow. Only one flag on foremast.

SZ 3 **\*\*\*\*\*\*\***

***STG 182*** "H.M.S. Majestic." Title woven below the bow. Two flags on foremast.

SZ 3 **\*\*\*\***

***STG 183*** "H.M.S. Magnificent." Title printed on mount. Two flags on foremast.

SZ 3 **\*\*\*\*\*\*\***

***STG 184*** "H.M.S. Victorious." Title printed on mount. Two flags on foremast.

SZ 3 **\*\*\*\*\*\*\***

STG 184

*STG 184a* No title at all, but similar gunboat to above, with one flag on foremast.
sz 3 ******

*STG 185* "H.M.S. Berwick." Title printed on mount. A three-funnelled gunboat sailing from right to left.
sz 3 *******

STG 185

## D. 2. COACHING

**London and York Coach**

*STG 186* "The 'London and York' Royal Mail Coach commenced running in the year 1706" printed above the silk picture and below it the words "From the Black Swan Holborn London to the Black Swan Coney Street York". This picture, with no rural background, was woven in the York Exhibition of 1879, which fact is often printed in the lower left corner, with Stevens' identification often printed in the lower right corner.
sz 1 (see picture page 90) **

**The Good Old Days**

*STG 187* "The Good Old Days." A stage-coach scene with no rural background. *See picture* p. 153.

SZ 1    TP    *

*STG 188* "The Good Old Days." The same coach picture as STG 187 but with a pleasant rural background woven in.

SZ 1    TP    LV    PC    *

**D. 3. FIRE ENGINES**

**For Life or Death**

*STG 189* "For Life or Death—Heroism on Land." An early steam fire-engine drawn by four horses, with an outrider, racing to a burning house. Variations of colour exist in the fire-engine and the men's clothing. *See picture* p. 153.

SZ 1    TP    **

*STG 190* "For Life or Death—Heroism on Land." A later steam fire-engine drawn by only two horses, with three boys and dog, racing to a burning cottage.

SZ 1    TP    ****

WOVEN IN PURE SILK.

*For Life or Death.*

HEROISM ON LAND.

STG 190

The Mersey Tunnel Railway.

**STG 191**

## D. 4. TRAINS

**Mersey Tunnel Railway**

*STG 191* "The Mersey Tunnel Railway." A sectional view of the tunnel with a train passing through, with sailing ships and boats above.

SZ 1     TP               *****

**The First Train**

*STG 192* "The First Train built by Geo. Stephenson in 1825." A "Rocket" type locomotive drawing a coal-car with two and a half open wagons. The wagons are coloured black and brown.

SZ 1     TP               ***

The First Train.

**STG 192**

STG 193

***STG 192a*** The same picture as STG 192 except that the wagons
are black and bright green.

sz 1     TP     ****

**Stephenson's Triumph**

***STG 193*** "Stephenson's Triumph, sixty miles an hour" printed
above the silk picture; underneath is printed "The First
Train ran on September 27th 1825 from Stockton to
Darlington". The colours of the train are the same as
STG 194. Usually woven in the York Exhibition of
1879.

sz 1     ***

**"The Present Time—60 miles per hour"** (Lord Howe train). This
title exists in several variations, as follows:

***STG 194*** "The Present Time." The two-carriage version. "60
miles per hour" is omitted. The front of the engine, the
funnel and the side of the coal-car are brown.

sz 1     TP     **

STG 194a

*STG 194a* "The Present Time 60 miles per hour." The two-carriage version. The front of the engine, the funnel and side of coal-car are in black. The two carriages are coloured red, blue, green, black and yellow.

SZ 1    TP                                                        *

*STG 194b* The same as STG 194a except that the two carriages have no red on them at all, being principally green and blue.

SZ 1    TP                                                      ***

*STG 195* "The Present Time 60 miles an hour." The two and a half carriage version.

SZ 1    TP                                                     ****

**More Modern Trains**

*STG 196* "The Present Time 60 miles per hour." A L.N.W.R. engine and two and a quarter carriages emerging from under a bridge on the right. Train travelling from right to left. Signals on left-hand side, and red flowering shrubs in foreground.

SZ 1    TP                                                       **

WOVEN IN PURE SILK BY THOMAS STEVENS, COVENTRY.

The Present Time.

60 Miles an Hour.

**STG 196**

*STG 197* "The Present Time." An eight-carriage train with L.N.W.R. Webb engine travelling from left to right. Tunnel in left background. Title often omitted, just "woven in pure silk" printed on mount.

sz 3   TP   PC   ✱✱✱✱✱

**Express Trains**

*STG 198* "The Present Time." A modern six-carriage express train travelling from left to right, with a tunnel in left background. Telegraph poles and trees in background. No driver leaning out of the cab.

sz 3   TP   LV   PC   ✱✱✱✱

*STG 198a* Same title and design as STG 198 except that the locomotive is a much larger type. The left bumper of the engine is level with the first telegraph pole and the driver is leaning out of the cab.

sz 3   TP   LV   ✱✱✱✱

*Note:* On late back labels, the title "Express Train" is often found and refers to STG 198 and 198*a*. No Stevengraph has been seen with "Express Train" printed on the mount. STG 198 and 198*a* appear with the usual "The Present Time" title or with no title at all.

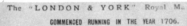

**STG 198**

**STG 200**

# COMBINATIONS

Two or more pictures or portraits are sometimes found in the same larger sized mount. The following combinations carry Stevens' identification, usually with one trade label stuck on the back:

**STG 199** "The Start" (STG 157) above and "The Finish" (STG 160) below. Pictures identical to the usual single copies.
TP                                                                    ******

**STG 200** "London and York Royal Mail Coach" (STG 186) above and "Stephenson's Triumph" (STG 193) below. The pictures and the titles are exactly the same as the usual single copies.
TP                                                                    ****

**STG 201** "London and York Royal Mail Coach" (STG 186) above and "Dick Turpin's last ride on his bonnie Black Bess" (STG 149) below. The pictures and titles are exactly the same as the usual single copies.
TP                                                                    ****

**STG 202** "Kaiser Wilhelm II" (STG 107) on the left, and "Augusta Victoria" (STG 100) on the right.
                                                                    *******

**STG 203** "Presdt. Cleveland" (STG 95) on the left and "Mrs. Cleveland" (STG 96) on the right. There are no flowers below Mrs Cleveland's portrait. Usually found as a cigarette advertisement with "Allen & Ginter's Richmond Straight Cut No. 1 Cigarettes are the best" printed on the mount.
TP                                                                    ******

It is believed that for some years Stevens obtained his cardboard mounts, already cut to shape and gilded, from the firm of T. E. Carter, Carver and Gilder of Coventry.

*STG 204* A rare combination exists with "The Good Old Days" (STG 187) silk ribbon at the top and "The Present Time" (STG 194) underneath with the words "The Good Old Days of Rattling Wheels and Gallant Greys" printed in the centre between the pictures. "The Present Time" is printed below the lower picture. The first letter of each word is coloured red and blue. Under the lower picture is printed "T. E. Carter, Carver and Gilder, Coventry".

sz $9\frac{1}{2}'' \times 11\frac{1}{2}''$        ******

This was most likely made by Carter with Stevens' permission for use as a trade sample of his firm's carving and gilding.

The following combinations have been noted, but they do not carry any Stevens' identification, no printed title and no trade label. They are listed for information purposes only.

1. "The Good Old Days" (STG 187) silk ribbon on the left, "George Stephenson" (STG 79) silk ribbon in the centre, and "The Present Time" (STG 198 or 198*a*) silk ribbon on the right.
2. "Death of Nelson" (STG 152) silk ribbon on the left, "Kitchener" (STG 45) silk ribbon in the centre, and "Wellington and Blucher" (STG 155) silk ribbon on the right.
3. "The Meet" (STG 165) silk ribbon on the left, "W. G. Grace" (STG 75) silk ribbon in the centre, and "The Death" (STG 167) silk ribbon on the right.

## MISCELLANEOUS

The following silk pictures and portraits are known to have been made by Stevens, but they have not been traced by the author in original mounts, thus suggesting that they were possibly made as tokens, or commemorative souvenirs: (see page 97)

H.R.H. The late Prince Consort and 5 daughters.
Her Majesty Queen Victoria and 4 sons.
Oxford Martyrs 1555–1556.
Bicentenary of the Act of Uniformity 1662.

The following silks were probably made by Stevens but the author has not seen any of them in original mounts with correct Stevens identification, while they do not appear on any of Stevens' sales lists:

Christopher Columbus, or 'Colon'.
Palace of Electricity, Paris.
Champs de Mars, Paris.
The Eiffel Tower, Paris.
Paris–Magazins du bon Marché.
Portrait of a man with a moustache, with blue cap, blue jacket, cream sleeves. Facing right. Believed to be Carl Hindenburg, President of the German Bicyclist.

---

# FRANK T. SABIN

## STEVENGRAPHS AVAILABLE
### ALSO
## FINE PRINTS
## DRAWINGS AND PAINTINGS

*9 Albemarle Street, London W.1*

---

While stocks last, copies of this book can be obtained from Michael Darby

---

# BOOKMARKERS

## PART II

# AN ALPHABETICAL LIST OF BOOKMARKERS MANUFACTURED BY THOMAS STEVENS

## by MICHAEL DARBY

The number of bookmarkers listed in this catalogue falls far short of the nine hundred different designs which Stevens claimed in his later advertisements to have produced. The author has studied all the largest collections of book-markers in the country but has only been able to list some 438 different ones.

Besides the obvious fact that many may not have survived, it seems prob-able that Stevens' total included small changes of pattern and colour in book-markers of the same subject. It certainly included ribbons which could not really be described as bookmarkers but rather as woven souvenirs. For example, in an advertisement in *The Bookseller*, January 31st, 1863, which is clearly headed "Stevens' Patent Illuminated Book Markers", number 80 is described as "Prince Albert and his daughters", and number 39 as "The Oxford Martyrs". Both ribbons measure some four inches by six inches and were probably intended as souvenirs.

Measurements have been included but can be very misleading. Though the width of bookmarkers bearing exactly similar subjects remains more or less constant, the length can vary by as much as one inch according to how hard the weft threads were beaten down in the loom during the weaving. Where different sizes of a particular subject are known to the author these have been included in the text. ALL MEASUREMENTS GIVEN ARE IN INCHES.

Colours have not been included except where they form the ground tint, as they too can be very misleading. There was no reason why the weaver should not introduce a shuttle of any colour he chose when another ran out of silk, and that new colours were introduced in this way undoubtedly happened quite frequently. The writer knows of many examples of bookmarkers with identical patterns appearing with numerous different colours. Furthermore the second half of the 19th century was a time of considerable experimentation with aniline dyes which had only just been discovered. Many were unstable and have either faded altogether now or literally changed colour. If colours have any importance it is the number used. Bookmarkers made in the early 1860's tend to have fewer colours than those made later in the century when improvements to the Jacquard loom facilitated the introduction of a greater number of shuttles. A more reliable guide to dating is provided by designs which were registered at the Patent Office, and by dated advertisements. These have both been mentioned in the text, though one must not forget that once sets of Jacquard cards were cut there was no reason why they should not be used over a number of years. Cards used in Lyons for weaving black and white pictures in the early 19th century still exist in the city.

97

The title of each bookmarker has been printed in capitals and where this does not make the subject clear it has either been printed in bold type or included in brackets. The first few words only of each lengthy piece of text have been included, and in one or two cases, the last few words too. Where variations of similar patterns are known to the author these have been mentioned.

1. ABERDEEN MUSICAL ASSOCIATION
1·6 × 7·2

2. ACCEPT THIS WITH MY BEST WISHES
2·0 × 9·3

3. AGNUS DEI
Narrow band.
Advertisement Oct. 31st, 1862; no. 10.

4. ALFRED DUKE OF EDINBURGH, CAPTAIN H.R.H.
2·0 × 8·3
Made for his wedding. See advertisement Dec. 1873.

5. AND WHEN SHE SAW THE ARK AMONG THE FLAGS SHE SENT HER MAID TO FETCH IT
2·1 × 11·1

6. ANY PROFESSION OF JESUS CHRIST WHICH BRINGS NO CROSS IS ALL NONSENSE
I don't care how near to the bottomless pit I go in order to save mankind.
Made for the Salvation Army.
2·6 × 8·1

7. ASCENSION, THE
I am the Resurrection and the Life saith the Lord.
2·1 × 9·4

8. AUFRICHTICHSTEN GLUCKWUNSCHE ZUM GEBURISFACE, DIE
1·6 × 6·7

9. AULD LANG SYNE
Should old acquaintance be forgot
Should old acquaintance be forgot and never brought . . .
2·2 × 9·4

10. AVE MARIA ORA PRO NOBIS
2·1 × 8·4

11. BABES IN THE WOOD

12. BEACONSFIELD, THE LATE EARL OF
Peace with honour.
1·8 × 3·8

13. BEATITUDES, THE
Blessed are the poor . . .
2·2 × 8·7

14. BEHOLD THE MAN
He was despised and rejected of men; a man of sorrows and
acquainted with grief.
2·2 × 11·4
It is possible that this bookmark may have appeared with the
alternative title "*Ecce Homo*", though the author has never
seen this version. See No. 184, I AM THE TRUE VINE.

15. BE KIND TO ONE ANOTHER
Charity thinketh no evil.
0·3 × 7·5

16. BESTEN WUNSCHE ZUM HEUTICHEN TAGE, DIE
On black and white grounds.
1·2 × 6·0 to 6·5

**Birthday greetings** (17–51)

17. BIRTHDAY
Love's offering.
Many happy returns of the day.

18. BIRTHDAY
Receive this token dearest friend . . .
1·6 × 4·4

19. BIRTHDAY, A
With music. See advertisement May 1st, 1871.

20. BIRTHDAY BLESSING
May peace enfold thee in her downy wing . . .
Best wishes.
2·2 × 9·0
Design registered 273958 June 25th, 1873.

21. BIRTHDAY BLESSING, A
Wishing you many happy returns of your birth . . .
On black and white grounds.
1·6 × 6·2

22. BIRTHDAY GIFT, A
Happy may thy birthday be, all hail to the day . . .
There are three variations:
A. With design of four diamonds at the pointed end.
8·0 × 2·1
B. With central floral device at the pointed end. 8·5 × 2·3
C. As A but with larger gaps at the top and bottom of the verse. 9·4 × 2·3

23. BIRTHDAY GREETING
On a loved one's birthday.
Many happy . . . by a sigh.
1·6 × 6·5

24. BIRTHDAY GREETING, A
This day once more I gladly hail . . .
1·6 × 5·7

25. BIRTHDAY PRESENT, A
Many happy returns of the day . . . heav'nly abode.
1·6 × 6·1

26. BIRTHDAY TOKEN, A
Let this pledge of earnest love . . .
1·2 × 4·9

27. BIRTHDAY WISH, A
A peaceful and a prosperous . .
1·6 × 5·11

28. BIRTHDAY WISH, A
Guidance for daily need . . .
$1\cdot7 \times 5\cdot2$

29. BIRTHDAY WISH, A
Happy may thy birthday be.
Many happy returns of the day . . . heav'nly abode.
$1\cdot6 \times 6\cdot4$

30. BIRTHDAY WISH, A
Many happy returns of the day . . . this can tell.
On black and white grounds.
$2\cdot1 \times 8\cdot8$ to $10\cdot0$

31. BIRTHDAY WISH, A
Many happy returns of the day . . . heav'nly abode.
$1\cdot6 \times 5\cdot4$ to $5\cdot7$

32. BIRTHDAY WISH, A
Many happy returns there is . . .
On black ground.
$2\cdot1 \times 11\cdot5$

33. BIRTHDAY WISH, A
May thy life be one summer . .
$1\cdot7 \times 7\cdot0$

34. BIRTHDAY WISHES
Joy greet the day that marks thy birth . .
On black and white grounds.
$1\cdot6 \times 6\cdot2$ to $6\cdot9$

35. GREETINGS AND BEST BIRTHDAY WISHES
Peace be around thee . . .
$1\cdot6 \times 5\cdot2$

36. HAPPY MAY THY BIRTHDAY BE
With design of five harebells.
On black and white grounds.
$1\cdot2 \times 5\cdot2$ to $5\cdot4$

101

37. HAPPY MAY THY BIRTHDAY BE
With design of a rose branch.
On black and white grounds.
1·1 × 5·5

38. HAPPY MAY THY BIRTHDAY (BEE)

39. HAPPY (MAY) THY BIRTHDAY BE
On black and white grounds.
2·1 × 9·3

40. HAPPY MAY THY BIRTHDAY BE
A happy birthday I wish thee . . .
On black ground.
2·1 × 11·0

41. HAPPY MAY THY BIRTHDAY BE
Many happy . . .
Design registered 255464 Sept. 11th, 1871.

42. HAPPY MAY THY BIRTHDAY BE
May peace be given unto thee, no care thy mind oppress . . .
On black, white and purple grounds.
1·6 × 6·9 to 8·4

43. HAPPY MAY THY BIRTHDAY BE
My heart breathes . . .
On black and white grounds.
2·1 × 8·5 to 9·0

44. HAPPY MAY YOUR BIRTHDAY (BEE) AND VERY
MANY MAY YOU SEE
On black and white grounds.
2·1 × 9·0 to 10·0

45. MAY EACH BIRTHDAY BE BRIGHTER THAN THE
LAST
1·6 × 6·1

46. MAY YOU HAVE A HAPPY BIRTHDAY AND MANY
OF THEM
1·2 × 5·5

47. MAY YOUR BIRTHDAY BE HAPPY
May hope with so propitious ray . . .
1·6 × 6·6

48. OH MAY THIS BIRTHDAY HAPPY BE AND VERY
MANY MAY YOU SEE
1·6 × 6·4

49. WISHING YOU A HAPPY BIRTHDAY
Let hope, sweet hope . . .
With best wishes.
1·6 × 6·1

50. WISHING YOU A HAPPY BIRTHDAY AND MANY
OF THEM
1·6 × 6·0

51. WITH LOVING WISHES FOR A HAPPY BIRTHDAY
I wish you happiness and peace . . .
2·1 × 8·0

52. BLESSED ARE THE MERCIFUL
1·6 × 6·6

53. BLESSING, A
At dawn of morn and close of day . . .
On a black ground.

54. BLESSING, A
Fear not ye for ye seek Jesus.

55. BLESSING, A
May Heaven's blessing e'er attend thee . .
1·5 × 4·9

56. BLESSING, A
May the morn of thy existence . . .
On black and white grounds.
1·6 × 6·2 to 6·4

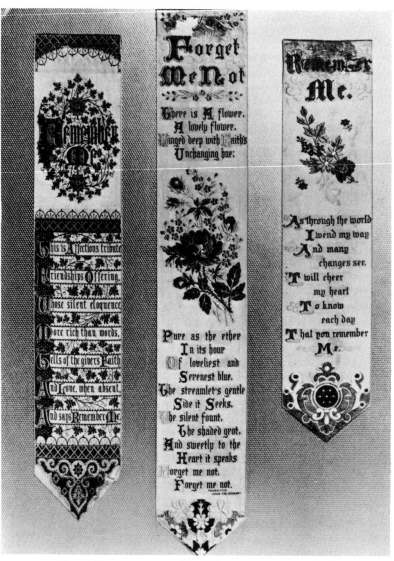

No. 304          No. 148          No. 301

57. BLESSING, A
May your progress in . . .
1·5 × 7·3

58. BLESSING, A
Oh fair and flowry . . . and those that love thee.
Blessings attend thee.
2·1 × 9·1
Design registered 274392, July 4th, 1873.

59. BLESSING, A
Oh fair and flowry . . . to be thee.
Blessings attend thee.

60. BOURNE, HUGH
Advertisement October 31st, 1862, nos. 55 and 56.

61. BRIDAY DAY, THY
Dear friends may this your wedding morn . . .
2·0 × 10·4

62. BRIDAL DAY, THY
Others dear girl may wish thee . . .
1·5 × 5·2
Design registered 157544, Nov. 19th, 1862.
Advertisement Dec. 6th, 1862, no. 66.
See *The Bookseller*, Dec. 6th, 1862, p. 750. "The success attending the Coventry bookmarkers noticed in our number for July last, has induced Mr. Stevens to prepare and issue a new series, which show a marked improvement both in design and in harmony of colours. Besides those intended for Bibles and Church services, we have others adapted to special occasions, anniversaries, etc., such as 'Bridal Day', 'Xmas', 'New Year's day', 'Birthday', and 'Love Tokens', etc. We find among them also mementoes to Robert Burns, Tributes to Garibaldi; with portraits etc. Very appropriately, too, there is one commemorative of Lady Godiva. Among the most effective we may distinguish those containing the Lord's Prayer, the Belief, Evening Hymn, the Busy Bee, and the Ten Commandments. The elegance and taste of these productions

105

H

must inevitably render them very popular and their manufacture will doubtless increase to such an extent as to become a most important feature of the industry of Coventry. The idea of their production is a happy one, and we hope they will obtain that measure of success to which they are justly entitled."

63. BRIGHT, THE RIGHT HONOURABLE JOHN, M.P.
1·6 × 5·8

64. BUNYAN
On purple, green and white grounds.
1·8 to 1·11 × 7·4 to 8·2
Design registered 152032, May 30th, 1862.
Advertisement Oct. 31st, 1862, no. 13.
See *The Bookseller*, July 31st, 1862, p. 467. "And lastly we have some prettily worked portraits in white and black silk, of Bunyan, Shakespeare, and John Wesley, worked with great fidelity and minuteness."
See *Coventry Herald and Observer*, Aug. 29th, 1862. "As Mr Stevens was the first so he continues to stand at the head of those manufacturers in our city who have devoted their attention to the production of those pretty little souvenirs which for want of a better we call by the name of bookmarkers. His portrait of Bunyan, with an exquisite little vignette of the house in which he was born is the best finished woven picture yet produced in Coventry. Also the portraits of Spurgeon, John Wesley, Cardinal Wiseman and others."
See *Coventry Herald and Observer*, Aug. 16th, 1862. "Others have historic sites such as the cottage of John Bunyan."

65. BURNS, ROBERT
Should old acquaintance be forgot . . .
1·8 × 7·2
Advertisement October 31st, 1862, no. 41
See *Coventry Herald and Observer*, October 10th, 1862. "The other is a portrait of Scotland's greatest poet also remarkable for the fidelity with which the draughtsman has transferred to a woven fabric the well known features of the author of 'Tam O'Shanter'. The portrait is in a medallion, above is a

verse from the song 'Auld Lang Syne'. Surrounding the bust are thistles, and the scroll inscribed with the titles of the most celebrated poems written by Burns, and underneath a charming little view of the cottage in which the immortal poet saw the light."

See *Coventry Herald and Observer*, Aug. 16th, 1862. "Others (bookmarkers) contain busts of Shakespeare, Burns etc."

66. BUSY BEE, THE
How doth the little busy bee . . .
1·6 × 6·0
Advertisement Oct. 31st, 1862, no. 42.
See no. 62 BRIDAL DAY, THY.

67. BUY YOUR OWN CHERRIES
The moral of the tale is this . . .
2·1 × 9·0

68. CALIFORNIA COMMANDERY, NO. 1, KT, SAN FRANCISCO
Pilgrimage to St. Louis Mo September 1886.
On a black ground.
2·5 × 8·2

69. CAST THY BREAD UPON THE WATERS
It shall be seen after many days.
1·6 × 4·0

70. CHARITY THINKETH NO EVIL

**Christmas Greetings** (71–93)

71. CHRISTMAS
A merry Christmas to you.
A blithe and joyous welcome . . .
2·1 × 8·8

72. A HAPPY CHRISTMAS
At this glad season of the year . . .
On black ground

73. A HAPPY CHRISTMAS
Dear Christmas . . .
Design registered 254390, Aug. 1st, 1871.

74. A HAPPY CHRISTMAS
Rise happy morn . . .
Glory to God in the highest.
Design registered 254388, Aug. 1st, 1871.

75. A HAPPY CHRISTMAS TO YOU
A happy Christmas I wish thee . . .
On black ground.
$2 \cdot 1 \times 11 \cdot 7$

76. A HAPPY CHRISTMAS TO YOU
God's angels stooped in bright array . . .
$2 \cdot 0 \times 9 \cdot 5$

77. MAY CHRISTMAS BRING THEE JOY
$0 \cdot 8 \times 5 \cdot 5$

78. MAY YOU HAVE A HAPPY CHRISTMAS AND MANY
OF THEM
$2 \cdot 1 \times 9 \cdot 2$

79. A MERRY CHRISTMAS
A blithe and joyous welcome . . .
$2 \cdot 2 \times 9 \cdot 0$

80. A MERRY CHRISTMAS
I heard the bells . . .
$2 \cdot 1 \times 12 \cdot 0$
Design registered 263763, June 25th, 1872.
It is interesting to note that this design which includes the
London to York stage coach was used as a bookmarker some
seven years before it was produced in a cardboard mount and
sold at the York Exhibition of 1879 as one of the first of
Stevens' pictures.

81. A MERRY CHRISTMAS AND A HAPPY NEW YEAR
Pointed at both ends.
$1 \cdot 6 \times 7 \cdot 0$

No. 84          No. 230          No. 405

82. A MERRY CHRISTMAS AND A HAPPY NEW YEAR
All hail to merry Christmas . . .
1·2 × 5·1

83. A MERRY CHRISTMAS AND A HAPPY NEW YEAR
A very merry Christmas and a happy new year, joy and
peace and happiness be ever with you here.

84. A MERRY CHRISTMAS AND A HAPPY NEW YEAR
Home for the holidays . . .
Design includes the locomotive "Lord Howe" with two coaches
2·1 × 12·3 (see page 109)

85. A MERRY CHRISTMAS AND A HAPPY NEW YEAR
I wish you . . .
Design registered 282160, May 6th, 1874.

86. MERRY CHRISTMAS AND A HAPPY NEW YEAR TO YOU
1·6 × 7·2

87. I WISH YOU A MERRY CHRISTMAS
1·6 × 4·5
Design on black ground registered 155448, Oct. 8th, 1862.
Design on white ground registered 155555, Oct. 10th, 1862.
It also occurs with a pink ground.
Advertisement Oct. 31st, 1862 no. 49.

88. I WISH YOU A MERRY CHRISTMAS
All hail to merry Christmas . . .
1·6 × 5·9

89. I WISH YOU A MERRY CHRISTMAS
Be your's unclouded mirth . . .
2·1 × 12·0

90. I WISH YOU A MERRY CHRISTMAS AND A HAPPY NEW YEAR
1·6 × 6·6
Design registered 157455, Nov. 15th, 1862.
Advertisement Dec. 6th, 1862, no. 64.

91. MAY YOU HAVE A HAPPY CHRISTMAS AND MANY OF THEM
On a black ground.
2·2 × 11·0

## 92. WISHING YOU A HAPPY CHRISTMAS
Here's Christmas come again . . .
1·5 × 6·0

## 93. WISHING YOU A MERRY CHRISTMAS AND A HAPPY NEW YEAR
On purple, black, and blue grounds.
2·1 × 9·3

## 94. COLLECT
Plain narrow band
0·3 × 8·2
Design registered 153243, July 17th, 1862; (this ribbon is joined with "HOLY COMMUNION", no. 103 and "PSALMS", no. 295).
Advertisement Oct. 31st, 1862, nos. 11 and 19.
Also made in a larger size see advertisement Dec. 6th, 1862, no. 67. See *The Bookseller*, July 31st, 1862, p. 467, for a brief mention.

## 95. COLLECT
Blessed Lord thou has caused . . .
1·7 × 8·7

### Chicago, World's Columbian Exhibition 1893 (96–101)
See Catalogue of the British Section, p. 152, no. 175, group LXXII, "Stevens, Thomas, Stevengraph Works, Coventry—Jacquard figure loom".

## 96. SOUVENIR OF THE DISCOVERY OF AMERICA
Woven in the World's Columbian Exposition Chicago 1893.
Columbus.
The *Santa Maria*.

## 97. SOUVENIR
Woven in the World's Columbian Exposition Chicago 1893.
Administration Building.
2·5 × 6·2

98. SOUVENIR
Woven in the World's Columbian Exposition Chicago 1893.
Machinery Hall.
2·5 × 6·5

99. SOUVENIR
Woven in the Columbian Exposition Chicago 1893.
The Star Spangled Banner . . .

100. SOUVENIR
Woven in the World's Columbian Exposition Chicago 1893.
U.S. Government Building.
2·5 × 6·5

101. 1492 1892 400TH ANNIVERSARY
In Commemoration of the Discovery Of America 1492.
Landing of Columbus Oct. 12th, 1492.
And the Star Spangled Banner . . .

102. COMMUNION
On pink ground.
1·3 × 8·8

103. COMMUNION, HOLY
0·3 × 8·2
Also produced in larger size see advertisement Dec. 6th, 1862, no. 67. See COLLECT no. 94.

104. COMPLIMENTS OF THE SEASON
Glory to God in the highest and on earth peace goodwill to men.
2·1 × 11·1

105. COMPLIMENTS OF THE SEASON, THE
I send to thee a greeting . . .
1·6 × 5·3

106. COMPLIMENTS OF THE SEASON, THE
May blessings rest on kindred . . .
Design registered 254387, Aug. 1st, 1871.

112

107. COMPLIMENTS OF THE SEASON, THE
Once again, once again . . .
Design registered 253939, July 10th, 1871.

108. COMPLIMENTS OF THE SEASON, THE
Winter is here let us welcome him on . . .
2·1 × 8·7
Design registered 253860, July 6th, 1871.

109. CONTENTMENT IS RICHES
Plain narrow band.
On purple ground.

110. COVENTRY FINE ART AND INDUSTRIAL
EXHIBITION
2·1 × 13·5
See *Royal Leamington Chronicle*, June 29th, 1867. "For the
present occasion as a memento of the Exhibition the loom is
producing one of the finest pieces of work that it has ever
turned out. There is a view of Coventry and of Stonleigh
Abbey top and bottom, and in the centre a striking bust of
Lord Leigh, the President of the Exhibition, with his coat of
Arms underneath. The colours are very brilliant, and the
views and likenesses remarkably correct. The machine is
indeed more truthful and graphic than many a painter."
For further accounts see *Royal Leamington Courier*, June
22nd, 1867; and the *Coventry Herald and Free Press*, July 5th,
1867.

111. CRANBOURNE M.P., VISCOUNT
Elected for the Darwen Division Dec. 2nd, 1885.

CREED, THE APOSTLE'S, see no. 185 I BELIEVE . .

112. (Cross)
Various coloured grounds.
1·1 to 1·3 × 14·6 to 18·0
Design registered 152036, and 152037, May 30th, 1862.
Advertisement Oct 31st, 1862, no. 9.

113. CRUCIFIXION, THE
Advertisement Oct 31st, 1862, nos. 20 and 26.

**Crystal Palace** (114–117)

114. MAY 5TH 1868 GREAT CHORAL FESTIVAL
Blue ground.
1·3 × 4·8

115. A PRESENT FROM THE CRYSTAL PALACE
On white and purple grounds.
2·2 × 9·4

116. HANDEL FESTIVAL
On blue ground.
1·2 × 6·0
See *The Young Englishwoman*, Jan. 1870, p. 39, for a brief mention.

117. WOVEN IN THE MACHINERY DEPARTMENT
CRYSTAL PALACE
The late Sir Joseph Paxton M.P. designer and architect of the Crystal Palace Sydenham.
2·1 × 10·0

118. DAVIES, ROBERT K. AND CO. NEW YORK
Novelties from England, France, China, Japan.
1·6 × 5·6

119. DEAREST I LOVE BUT THEE
1·6 × 5·3

120. DEAREST I LOVE BUT THEE
Hail to love to mighty love . . .
1·6 × 5·8

121. DEAR FRIEND'S WISH, A
Where'er your abode . . .
Friendship's offering.
2·1 × 8·9

122. DEVOTED LOVE
I go with thee, I will be thine . .
1·6 × 5·0

123. DICKENS, CHARLES
Born Feb. 7th, 1812, Died June 9th, 1870, Buried . . .

124. DISRAELI, RT. HON. B., M.P.
First Lord of the Treasury 1868.
1·7 × 5·7

125. DOXOLOGY, THE
Pointed at both ends on blue and white grounds.
1·5 × 7·0
Design registered 157276, Nov. 11th, 1862.
Advertisement Dec. 6th, 1862, no. 60.

126. DUBLIN, INTERNATIONAL EXHIBITION
Inaugurated by His Royal Highness The Prince of Wales,
May 9th, 1865.
2·0 × 10·5
Design registered 185596, April 3rd, 1865.

127. ECCE AGNUS DEI
There are three variations:
A. Inscribed at top as drafted by Welch and Lenton. 1·1 ×
14·0. Designs registered 152038, and 152034, May 30th,
1862.
B. On green ground with two floral devices at the bottom.
1·4 × 7·6
C. On green ground with two crosses at the bottom. 1·3 ×
12·0
See *The Bookseller*, July 31st, 1862, p. 467. "Amongst those
ready are some intended for folio bibles and prayer books.
One with *Agnus Dei* beautifully worked in coloured silks,
and an inscription upon a different coloured ribbon; another
without the inscription; while the third has simply the cross
worked in green and gold colour upon a purple ground. All
have rich bullion silk fringes."

128. ENGLAND'S JOY
Celebrates the Marriage of Edward and Alexandra in 1863.
1·5 × 5·9
Advertisement Mar 31st, 1863, no. 89.

129. EVER DEAREST EVER NEAREST

130. FAITH HOPE AND CHARITY
Rock of ages cleft . . .
2·1 × 9·0
Design registered 273605, June 11th, 1873.

131. FADER WÅR
1·6 × 7·1

132. FAMILY WORSHIP
Cotter's Saturday night.
They never sought in vain that sought the Lord aright.
10·2 × 2·1

133. FELICIDADES$^y$ RECUERDO
1·1 × 5·3

134. FELIZ ANO NUEVO
On red and black grounds.
0·7 × 5·4 to 5·6

135. FOR A GOOD BOY
Design registered 282118, between Feb. and May, 1874.

136. FOR A GOOD GIRL
Design registered 281983, between Feb. and May, 1874.

137. FOR AULD LANG SYNE
1·2 × 5·6

138. FORGET ME NOT
Very narrow band; red, purple, and black grounds.

139. FORGET ME NOT
Design includes flowers and a piece of wood.
2·0 × 8·4

140. FORGET ME NOT
Wording in the centre of the ribbon with bands at top and bottom.
1·5 × 5·0

141. FORGET ME NOT
Narrow ribbon, floral design in the middle.

142. FORGET ME NOT
Dost thou think I can forget thee . . .
2·1 × 9·4

143. FORGET ME NOT
Forget thee? Bid the sun . . .
2·2 × 9·9
Design registered 274597, July 21st, 1873.

144. FORGET ME NOT
Forget thee? not while . . .
1·6 × 6·5

145. FORGET ME NOT
May heaven's blessings be with thee and with me.
On black ground.
2·1 × 9·7

146. FORGET ME NOT
Ne'er from thy heart my memory blot . . .
1·6 × 5·4

147. FORGET ME NOT
Reflecting from the sky its tint . . .
Forget me not.
1·5 × 8·4

148. FORGET ME NOT
There is a flower a lovely flower . . . (see page 104)
2·1 × 11·1

149. FORGET ME NOT
Though absent not forgotten the mighty . .
1·5 × 8·5

150. FORGET ME NOT
Forget me not.
Time cannot change or alter . . .
1·2 × 5·0

151. FRIENDS BENEDICTION, A
A token of esteem.
May the blessings of thy God . . .
2·1 × 8·2

152. FRIENDS BLESSING, A
May the blessing of thy God . . .
2·0 × 8·6

153. FRIENDSHIP
From a true friend.
How sweet the bonds of friendship . . .
1·6 × 4·7

154. GARIBALDI
Freedom for Italy Rome or death.
Design includes the Castle of Spezzia.
2·1 × 9·3
Advertisement Oct 31st, 1862, nos. 43, 48, 57.
See *Coventry Herald and Observer*, Oct. 10th, 1862. "Two
other portraits to add to Mr Stevens' list. One is a striking
likeness to Garibaldi; underneath which is a splendid view of
the castle of Spezzia—sharp and clear as a steel engraving."
See also no. 62 BRIDAL DAY, THY.

155. GARIBALDI
Freedom for Italy Rome or death.
The hero of Palermo . . .
2·1 × 7·2

156. GARIBALDI
United Italy Rome or death.
1·5 × 6·1

157. GLADSTONE, RT HON. W. E., M.P.
Economy, Retrenchement, Reform.
1·6 × 5·3

158. GLOUCESTER LIFE BOAT, THE
1·7 × 5·3

159. GOD IS GOOD
Morn amid the mountains . . .

160. GOD IS LOVE
Narrow, on red and green grounds.

**Godiva Lady** (161–162)

161. PEEPING TOM
Then she rode back . . .
Lady Godiva.
2·2 × 10·5
See no. 62, BRIDAL DAY, THY.
Illustrated in *Country Life*, Nov. 1955.

162. GODIVA, LADY
Ye faire Ladie Godiva and Peeping Tom of the Anciente
Citye of Coventre.
1·7 × 6·6
Advertisement Oct. 31st, 1862, no. 44
Illustrated in W. Baker, *The Silk Pictures of Thomas Stevens*,
p. 95, fig. 40.

163. GRANT, GENERAL U.S. RICHMOND 1865 VICKS-
BURG FORT DONELSON
1·6 × 5·2

164. GRANT, LIEUTENANT GENERAL U.S. RICHMOND
1865
2·1 × 10·2

165. GREETING
Wishing you prosperity and health.
1·2 × 5·5

166. GUTHRIE, DR
Blessed is he that considereth the poor.
1·8 × 8·6

167. HAPPY LOVE
Come let us stray our gladsome way . . .
2·1 × 10·5

168. HAPPY MAY THY FUTURE BE
2·2 × 9·1

169. HERZLICHEN GLUCKWUNSCH
On black and white grounds.
2·1 × 11·2 to 11·5

170. HERZLICHEN WUNSCHE, DIE
On black ground.
2·1 × 9·4

171. HOLD ON IN THE DARK
In the very face of death hold on! have patience, hold on!
Made for the Salvation Army.
2·6 × 8·6

172. HOME SWEET HOME
Mid pleasures and palaces . . .
There are four variations:
A. With music and "Home Sweet Home" written below the picture of the house. 2·1 × 9·8 to 11·0.
B. Without music and "Home Sweet Home" written at the very top of the ribbon. 2·1 × 8·7.
C. As "B" but with a line of leaves and flowers above the words "Home Sweet Home".
D. Altogether different from "A", "B", and "C". A different house is featured in the middle of the ribbon. There is no music. 1·7 × 7·4.
"A" is mentioned in Advertisement dated May 1st, 1871 under the heading "Stevens new series of Musical Book-markers".

173. HONOUR THY FATHER AND MOTHER
1·6 × 7·8

174. HOPE, ADMIRAL SIR JAMES, G.C.B.
H.M.S. *Duncan.*
Deeds not words.
2·1 × 9·3

175. HOPE AT ALL TIMES
2·1 × 9·4

176. HOPE THE (ANCHOR) OF THE SOUL
The Lord bless thee . . .
2·1 × 8·3

177. HYMN, CHRISTMAS
While shepherds watched . . .
1·7 × 5·8
Design registered 157456, Nov. 15th, 1862.
Advertisement Dec. 6th, 1862, no. 65.

178. HYMN, EASTER
Jesus Christ is risen today . . .
1·8 × 7·6
Advertisement Jan. 31st, 1863, no. 86.

179. HYMN, EVENING
And now another day is gone . . .
1·7 × 6·7
Advertisement Oct. 31st, 1862, no. 52.
See no. 62 BRIDAL DAY, THY.

180. HYMN, EVENING
Glory to thee . . .
1·7 × 6·7
Advertisement Dec. 6th, 1862, no. 63.

181. HYMN, MORNING
By Watts.
Advertisement Jan. 31st, 1863, no. 79.

182. HYMN, MORNING
Awake my soul . . .
1·7 × 6·7
Advertisement Mar. 31st, 1863, no. 91.

183. I AM THE LIGHT OF THE WORLD
1·6 × 6·0

184. I AM THE TRUE VINE
I am the bread of life, do this in remembrance of me.
2·1 × 10·3
See *The Reliquary*, Vol. XII, 1871–72, p. 182. "To our minds however, three now before us, viz:—'I am the true vine', 'We praise thee O God' with the celebrated picture of chorister boys; and '*Ecce Homo*' ('He was despised and rejected of men') are the greatest achievements of the Textile art we have seen; and are worthy of preservation. The head of Our Saviour in the latter is unsurpassable in expression, in delicacy of work, and in power of conception either by the graver or the pencil—it is rather a true work of art, and one of which Mr Stevens may justifiably be proud."

185. I BELIEVE IN GOD . . .
There are two variations:
A. With gothic arch at the top. 1·7 × 9·1.
B. With inverted heart at the top. 2·1 × 8·0.
Advertisement Oct. 31st, 1862, no. 30.
See no. 263 NATIONAL ANTHEM.
See also no. 62 BRIDAL DAY, THY.

186. ICH GRATULIRE
1·5 × 7·4

187. I HAD A LITTLE DOGGY

188. IHS
The tops and bottoms of the letters form scrolling decoration.
1·5 × 8·6
Advertisement Oct. 31st, 1862, no. 51.

189. I LOVE LITTLE PUSSY
I love little pussy her coat . . .
$1.6 \times 6.8$

190. IN MEMORIAM
With kind wishes
Blessed are they that mourn for they shall be comforted.
$1.6 \times 6.0$

191. I WAS GLAD . . .
Advertisement Oct. 31st, 1862, no. 27—"Three bands with passages of Scripture, 'I was glad' etc."

192. I WILL BLESS THE LORD AT ALL TIMES
joined with O LORD LET THY MERCY LIGHTEN UPON US
Each $0.6 \times 8.7$

193. JACKSON, THE LATE GENERAL "STONEWALL"
Died May 9, 1863.
Know ye not . . .
$2.1 \times 8.5$

194. JAMES, JOHN ANGELL
$1.5 \times 7.6$
Advertisement Oct. 31st, 1862, no. 47.

195. JAMES, THE LATE JOHN ANGELL
Advertisement Oct. 31st, 1862, no. 40.

196. JE SUIS L'IMMACULEE CONCEPTION
Conceptio immaculata sum.
$2.4 \times 10.5$

197. JESUS DIED FOR ALL
Narrow band on blue ground.

198. JESUS HEAR AND SAVE
God of pity God of grace.
$2.1 \times 9.1$

199. JESUS SAID SUFFER LITTLE CHILDREN . . .
1·6 × 9·8
Design registered 158875, Jan. 5th, 1862.

200. KNOX, JOHN
1·5 × 7·2
Advertisement Oct. 31st, 1862, nos. 37 and 38.

201. LAST ROSE OF SUMMER, THE
There are two variations:
A. Without music. 2·1 × 8·8
B. With music. 2·2 × 9·4
Design registered 252190, May 4th, 1871.
See no. 278 THE OLD ARM CHAIR
Advertisement May 1st, 1871, under heading "Stevens new series of Musical Bookmarkers".

302. LEARN TO DO WELL
Narrow plain band.
Green and blue grounds.

203. LEO POPE P. XIII
1·6 × 4·5

204. LESSON I
On pink ground.
1·3 × 8·9

205. LESSON II
On mauve ground.
1·3 × 9·4
See *The Coventry Herald and Observer*, Aug. 16th, 1862. "The greater number are for special purposes Prayer Books etc. Several bands united and yet detached are so marked as to indicate the Litany, Lessons, and so forth."

206. LET THE PEOPLE PRAISE THEE O GOD
Advertisement Oct. 31st, 1862, no. 6.
See *The Bookseller*, July 31st, 1862, p. 467. "There are also two sets intended for church services, one with the same inscription worked on each of the six ribbons, 'Let the people praise thee O God'."

207. LILY, THE
The lily should the emblem be of that same love I feel for thee. Morn impearl thy leaves . . .

208. LINCOLN PRESIDENT

209. LINCOLN, THE LATE LAMENTED PRESIDENT
$2 \cdot 0 \times 9 \cdot 3$

210. LITANY
On pink ground.
$1 \cdot 4 \times 7 \cdot 9$
Advertisement Dec. 6th, 1862, no. 67.
See nos. 204 and 205, LESSONS I and II

211. LITTLE BOY BLUE
$6 \cdot 7 \times 1 \cdot 6$
Design registered 282396, May 18th, 1874.

212. LITTLE BO PEEP
Little Bo Peep has lost her sheep . . .

213. LITTLE BUSY BEE, THE
On blue ground.
$1 \cdot 7 \times 7 \cdot 6$

214. LITTLE JACK HORNER
Design registered 282846, June 9th, 1874.

215. LITTLE RED RIDING HOOD
$1 \cdot 6 \times 6 \cdot 0$
Design registered 262431, between Feb. and June, 1872.

216. LITTLE SAMUEL
Advertisement Jan. 31st, 1863, no. 76.

217. LOOK OF LOVE, THE
Ever dearest ever nearest naught from thee my love can part. 'Tis not the lily brow I prize . . .
There are three variations:
A. With lovers knot and surround to the verse. $2 \cdot 1 \times 10 \cdot 2$
B. Without above. $2 \cdot 1 \times 8 \cdot 7$
C. With "Look of Love" written at the very top, and a floral branch down the left hand side.

I*

218. LORD BE MERCIFUL UNTO THEE AND BLESS THEE,
THE
On black and white grounds.
$1·2 \times 5·2$

219. LORD BLESS YOU, THE
Narrow band.
On cream and blue grounds.

220. LORD BLESS THEE, THE
Narrow band.
On white and blue grounds.

221. LORD IS MY SHEPHERD, THE
I shall not want.
There are two variations:
A. With wording on a diamond patterned ground. $1·5 \times 6·3$
B. With wording on a floral patterned ground. $1·6 \times 7·3$
Advertisement Jan 31st, 1863, no. 83.

222. LORD IS MY SHEPHERD, THE
The Lord my pasture shall prepare . . .
$1·5 \times 6·2$

LORD'S PRAYER, THE (see no. 283 OUR FATHER . . .)

223. LOVE
Affections fond remembrancer.
$1·6 \times 5·2$

224. LOVE
Art thou not dear unto my heart . . .
$1·5 \times 5·2$

225. LOVE
The blossoms in the bowers . . .
On white and brown grounds.
$1·6 \times 5·3$

226. LOVE
Unchanging love
Though absent parts for a while . . .
$1·5 \times 7·4$

227. LOVE'S EMBLEM
True love fadeth never . . .
Flowers fade . . .
1·6 × 4·5

228. LOVE'S OFFERING
Love's offering, aye! what should it be? . . .
1·2 × 5·5

229. LOVE'S THOUGHTS

230. MAIL COACH
We're losing fast the good old days . . .
The design includes the London to York stage coach.
2·1 × 12·0
See no. 80 A MERRY CHRISTMAS.

231. MANY HAPPY RETURNS OF THE DAY
Narrow ribbon.
On black and mauve grounds.
0·4 × 5·5

232. MANY HAPPY RETURNS OF THE DAY
Wording on a drape in a central roundel.
1·5 × 4·9

233. MANY HAPPY RETURNS OF THE DAY
Another year is added . . .
On black and white grounds.
1·5 × 6·1

234. MANY HAPPY RETURNS OF THE DAY
Many happy returns of the day . . . today.
Design includes a balloon.

235. MANY HAPPY RETURNS OF THE DAY
Many happy returns of the day . . . forgetful of me.
Design reistered 280838, Feb. 28th, 1874.

236. MANY HAPPY RETURNS OF THE DAY
May all thy . . .
On black ground.
1·2 × 5·2

237. MANY HAPPY RETURNS OF THE DAY
May its presence . . .
1·5 × 6·8

238. MANY HAPPY RETURNS OF THE DAY
Merry words, Merry words ye come . . .
2·1 × 9·5 to 11·5

239. MAY BLESSINGS ATTEND THEE
The Lord bless thee and keep thee . . .
1·6 × 5·6

240. MAY BLESSINGS ATTEND THEE
Your life for many years to come . . .
1·2 × 5·6

241. MAY HAPPINESS BE EVER THINE
On black ground.
1·2 × 5·9

242. MAY HEALTH AND HAPPINESS BE THINE
I wish thee happiness . . .
2·1 × 9·4

243. MAY HEAVEN'S BLESSINGS BE WITH YOU
Ecce Homo.
1·7 × 6·0

244. MAY OUR HEARTS BE UNITED IN LOVE FOREVER
1·6 × 5·0

245. MAY OUR HEARTS BE UNITED
O learn to love the lesson is but plain . . .

246. MAY OUR HEARTS BE UNITED
Tell me not of sparkling gems set in regal diadems . . .
2·1 × 9·3

247. MAY THE BESTOWER OF ALL BLISS GRANT THEE
YEARS OF HAPPINESS
On black and white grounds.
2·1 × 9·4 to 9·7

248. MAY THE GIVER AND RECEIVER MEET IN HEAVEN
1·6 × 5·8 (illustration page 130)

249. MAY THE GIVER AND RECEIVER MEET IN HEAVEN
Faith grasped the cross . . .
2·1 × 11·5

250. MAY THE GIVER AND RECEIVER MEET IN HEAVEN
Sweet and peaceful be thy life . . .
On black and white grounds.
2·1 × 9·3

251. MAY THE GIVER EVER DWELL IN THY MEMORY
Oh be thou blest . . .
On black and white grounds.
1·6 × 8·0

252. MAY THY LIFE BE FULL OF JOY
Every blessing here attend you.

253. MEMBER OF THE OPEN AIR MISSION
0·6 × 11·5

254. MILLER, REV. J. C., D.D., RECTOR OF ST. MARTINS BIRMINGHAM
1·5 × 6·7
Advertisement Oct. 31st, 1862, nos. 32 and 33.

255. MISTRESS MARY QUITE CONTRARY
1·6 × 6·5 to 6·8

256. MIZPAH
The Lord watch between me and thee when we are absent one from another.
There are two variations:
A. With design of fuschia on black and white grounds.
1·6 × 6·0 (illustration page 130)
B. With design of convolvulus on black and white grounds.
2·1 × 8·5 to 9·2

257. MUCHAS FELICIDADES
1·6 × 6·5

## 258. MUTUAL BOND, THE
Our mutual bond of faith and truth . . .
Bound with affection.
2·1 × 9·2

No. 256a          No. 256a

No. 14          No. 248          No. 338

259. MY DEAR FATHER
Mid all the mercies of this life . . .
On blue ground.
1·6 × 6·0

260. MY DEAR FATHER
Much there is of joy on earth . . .
1·6 × 7·4

261. MY DEAR MOTHER
Whate'er my lot in life may be . . .
1·6 × 5·8 to 7·5

262. MY SOUL DOTH MAGNIFY THE LORD . . .
With music.
Advertisement May 1st, 1871.

263. NATIONAL ANTHEM
God save our gracious . . .
On purple and pink grounds.
1·7 × 10·4
Design registered 153241, July 17th, 1862.
Advertisement Oct. 31st, 1862, no. 18.
See *The Coventry Herald and Observer*, Aug. 29th, 1862.
"To this class belong three exquisite pieces of woven lettering
'The Lords Prayer', 'The Apostle's Creed', and 'The National
Anthem', all of them are finished with exquisite care and
good taste. The 'National Anthem' has 'Victoria' worked in
a very neat monogram among the tracery underneath the
verses."

**New Year's Greetings** (264–274)

264. NEW YEAR
A happy new year to you.
A blithe and joyous welcome . . .
2·1 × 8·8

265. NEW YEAR'S AULD LANG SYNE
Time ever on the wing . . .
With good wishes.
2·1 × 9·0

266. NEW YEAR'S GREETINGS
As hand grasps hand . . .
2·1 × 8·11

267. NEW YEAR'S WISHES
A happy year . . .
Design registered 253666, June 30th, 1871.

268. A HAPPY NEW YEAR
A new year tis a pleasant sound . . .
Design registered 254389, Aug. 1st, 1871.

269. A HAPPY NEW YEAR
May blessings rest on kindred and on friends . . .
1·6 × 5·4

270. A HAPPY NEW YEAR
Ring out . . .
Design registered 253665, June 30th, 1871.

271. I WISH YOU A HAPPY NEW YEAR
On a blue ground.
1·7 × 4·11
Advertisement Oct. 31st, 1862, no. 60.

272. WITH BEST WISHES FOR THE NEW YEAR
On a black ground.
1·6 × 8·0

273. WITH BEST WISHES FOR THE NEW YEAR
Oh be thou blest with all that . . .
On a black ground.

274. WITH GOOD WISHES FOR THE NEW YEAR
She gladly read unto the blind . . .
Same design as no. 215 LITTLE RED RIDING HOOD

275. NO CROSS NO CROWN

276. NO ME OLVIDES
On black, red and mauve grounds.
0·7 × 5·2 to 5·7

277. NORWICH CONNECTICUT
The rose of New England.
250th anniversary of the founding of the town ..
2·1 × 9·2

278. OLD ARM CHAIR, THE
There are three variations:
A. With chair at the top of the ribbon.
Design registered 252190, May 4th, 1871.
B. With chair in the middle of the verse. 2·0 × 9·5
C. With music.

Advertisement May 1st, 1871.
See *The Reliquary*, Vol. XII, 1871–72, p. 182. "Another series has on each bookmark the entire series music and words of popular songs and ballads; among these are Eliza Cook's "Old Arm Chair", Moore's "Last Rose of Summer", and others, with appropriate designs, among which the "Old Arm Chair" with its finely carved back, is one of the most successful efforts of the weaver's art we have seen."
See also *The Coventry Standard*, June 28th, 1873. "The other loom is engaged in weaving twelve breadths at once of a bookmark on which Eliza Cook's copy of the 'Old Arm Chair' is produced. The lettering and notation are admirably 'put on' for the loom but the pictorial perspective of the chair as the headpiece, is out of harmony with the treatment adopted for the essential portion of the subject."

279. O LORD HAVE MERCY UPON US
2·1 × 11·4 to 11·8

280. OUR CHOICE FOR PRESIDENT AND VICE
PRESIDENT 1888
2·5 × 5·2

281. OUR CHOICE FOR PRESIDENT AND VICE
PRESIDENT 1888
Rival candidates.
2·5 × 5·9

282. OUR CHOICE FOR PRESIDENT AND VICE
PRESIDENT
First ones.
$2.0 \times 5.5$

283. OUR FATHER WHICH ART IN HEAVEN . . .
On black ground.
$1.7 \times 8.1$
Advertisement Oct. 31st, 1862, no. 22.
See no. 263 NATIONAL ANTHEM and no. 62 BRIDAL
DAY, THY

284. OUR SAVIOUR
This do in remembrance of me.
$1.5 \times 6.6$ to $7.2$
Advertisement Oct. 31st, 1862, no. 34 and 35.

285. OVERCOME EVIL WITH GOOD

286. OXFORD, RT. REV. LORD BISHOP OF
$2.2 \times 8.7$
Mar. 31st, 1863, no. 94.

287. PIKE, J. G.
Advertisement Oct. 31st, 1862, nos. 58 and 59.

288. PIKE, J. G., THE LATE REV.
$1.5 \times 7.2$

289. PIUS IX
$1.6 \times 6.9$
Advertisement October 31st, 1862, nos. 28 and 31.

290. POWER OF LOVE, THE
Solomon says many waters . . .
$1.6 \times 7.1$

291. PRAISE WAITETH FOR THEE

292. PRAY WITHOUT CEASING
Narrow band black and blue grounds.

293. PRAYER
On blue ground.
1·8 × 6·5

294. PRAYERS and IHS repeated.
Narrow plain band.
Design registered 152035, May 30th, 1862.
This design was copied by another Coventry firm Mulloney
and Johnson. See *Coventry Herald and Observer*, Oct. 24th,
1862.

295. PSALMS
On green ground.
1·3 × 8·8
Advertisement Dec. 6th, 1862, no. 67.
See no. 94 COLLECT.

296. QUIRK, THE REV. J. R., M.A.
With Attleborough Church and the Parsonage.
2·1 × 11·8
The picture of the Parsonage is the same as that which appears
on no. 172 HOME SWEET HOME.

297. RAIKES, ROBERT
(Founder of Sunday Schools)
Design registered 349796, May 12th, 1880.

298. READ, MARK, LEARN AND INWARDLY DIGEST
0·4 × 7·2
Advertisement Oct. 31st, 1862, no. 36.

299. REDEEMER, THE
And when Jesus had cried . . .
1·5 × 8·9
Design registered 153382, July 31st, 1862.
Taken from the Van Dyke in the National Gallery.
This ribbon was copied by another Coventry firm Mulloney
and Johnson. See *The Coventry Herald and Observer*, Oct.
24th, 1862.

300. REMEMBER ME
As on this little gift you gaze . . .
1·6 × 5·9 to 6·3

301. REMEMBER ME
As through the world I wend my way . . .
On black and white grounds.
2·1 × 9·0 to 9·2 (illustration page 104)

302. REMEMBER ME
Long bloom upon thy cheek the (rose) and (violet) be thy lot.
And when new friends around thee throng . . .
1·6 × 7·5
Design registered 260669, Feb. 23rd, 1872.

303. REMEMBER ME
There's not a look a word of thine . . .
2·1 × 9·6

304. REMEMBER ME
This is affection's tribute . . . (illustration page 104)
2·1 × 11·0

305. REMEMBER ME
Tis sweet . . .
There are two variations:
A. With convolvulus design. 1·6 × 5·8
B. With rose design. 1·6 × 6·5

306. REMEMBER NOW THY CREATOR IN THE DAYS OF
THY YOUTH
There are two variations:
A. With gothic arch above the words, on blue ground. 1·8
× 8·7
B. With ogival arch above the words. 2·1 × 8·8
Advertisement Jan. 31st, 1863, no. 78.

307. REMEMBER THE SABBATH DAY TO KEEP IT HOLY
1·6 × 6·3

308. RESURRECTION, THE
I am the resurrection and the Life saith the Lord.
1·7 × 8·4
Advertisement April 30th, 1863, no. 96.

309. RIDE A COCK HORSE
Design registered 283906, July 24th, 1874.

310. SAILOR BOY, THE
The world below hath not for me . . .
2·1 × 10·4

311. SAINT BERNARD COMMANDERY
No. 35 Knight Templar Chicago 1880.
2·4 × 6·8

312. SANCTA MARIA
Narrow band.
Advertisement Oct. 31st, 1862, no. 5.

313. SCOTT
Kenilworth Castle 1863.
1·6 × 8·8
Advertisements Jan. 31st, 1863, no. 85, and March 31st, 1863, no. 87.

314. SEVENTH REGIMENT EXPOSITION 1879
1·5 × 5·5

**Shakespeare, William** (315–324)

315. SHAKESPEARE
He so sepulchred in such pomp doth lie . . .
Design includes portrait of Shakespeare and pictures of Stratford Church, and the poet's birthplace in floral rosettes.
2·1 × 11·0

316. SHAKESPEARE
He so sepulchred in such pomp doth lie . . .
Design includes portrait of Shakespeare in floral rosette.

No. 321          No. 317          No. 323

317. SHAKESPEARE

He so sepulchred in such pomp doth lie . . .
He was a man take him for all . . .
Design includes a portrait of Shakespeare and pictures of
Stratford Church and the birthplace of the poet.
2·1 × 11·0 (illustration page 138)

318. SHAKESPEARE

OBIT ANO DOI 1616 AETAT 53 DIE 23 AP
He was not for an age but for all time.
2·0 × 5·0
Advertisement Oct. 31st 1862 no. 12.
See no. 64 BUNYAN.

319. SHAKESPEARE, STRATFORD, BIRTHPLACE

Separate narrow bands joined each 0·8 × 11·5

320. SHAKESPEARE'S TERCENTENARY
COMMEMORATION APRIL 23, 1864

The Bard of Avon. (illustration page 138)
The Poet's birthplace.
Stratford Church.
Three separate ribbons not really intended as bookmarkers
but to be joined together to form a favour.
2·1 × 6·0
See *Derby Mercury*, March 30th, 1864. "We have received
from Mr Thomas Stevens samples of his beautifully worked
favours for the Shakespeare Tercentenary. . . . They are
marvellously worked and are undoubtedly the best specimens
of weaving we have seen."
See also *Derbyshire Advertiser and Journal*, April 1st, 1864;
*The Queen*, April 2nd, 1864; *Leeds Mercury*, April 29th,
1864; *The Young Englishwoman*, Jan. 1870, p. 39.

321. SHAKESPEARE'S TERCENTENARY 1864

Shakespeare.
He was a man take him for all in all . . . (illustration page 138)

322. As above but without the words "Shakespeare's Tercentenary
1864".
1·7 × 6·11

323. As no. 321 but with Shakespeare's birthplace at the bottom. (illustration page 138)

324. Narrow striped band with portrait at each end.

325. SHAW RICHD ESQR M.P.
The choice of the working men and . . .
2·0 × 9·6 to 10·5

326. SILKEN ALPHABET, THE
On blue and black grounds.
1·7 × 7·3 to 7·7
Advertisement Jan. 31st, 1863, no. 77.

327. SOMMERS LETZTE ROSE
2·0 × 9·3

328. THE SOUL WINNERS GUIDE OR HOW TO DEAL WITH SPECIAL CLASSES
1·6 × 5·2

329. SPEED WELL REMEMBER ME AND I'LL REMEMBER THEE
2·0 × 8·5

330. SPURGEON
We preach not ourselves but Christ Jesus the Lord.
There are two variations:
A. Portrait facing slightly left without beard. Design registered 152686, June 23rd, 1862. Advertisement Oct. 31st, 1862, nos. 15 and 23.
B. Portrait facing right with beard.

331. STAR SPANGLED BANNER, THE
Oh say can you . . .
2·3 × 9·3

332. SYDNEY, A PRESENT FROM
2·1 × 9·3

333. TEMPLARS PLEDGE IS FOR LIFE, THE
Wine is a mocker strong drink is raging.
Touch not—Taste not—Handle not.
Faith Hope and Charity.
2·1 × 8·7 to 9·0
Design registered 289684.

334. TEN COMMANDMENTS, THE
Thou shalt have no . . .
1·6 × 9·3
Advertisement Dec. 6th, 1862, no. 61.
See no. 62 BRIDAL DAY, THY.

335. TESTAMENT, NEW
On a pink ground.
0·3 × 8·2

336. TESTAMENT, OLD
On green ground.
0·3 × 8·2
Advertisement Jan. 31st, 1863, no. 71.

337. THOU ART LOVELY
Thy beauty wins my heart . . .
1·5 × 4·7

338. THY WILL BE DONE ON EARTH AS IT IS HEAVEN
2·1 × 9·6 to 10·9 (illustration page 130)

339. TO A BROTHER
Advertisement April 30th, 1863, no. 101.

340. TO A DEAR ONE
To a dear one.
Could I bring this . . .
1·2 × 4·9

341. TO A FRIEND
Happy be thou my dearest . .
1·8 × 6·6 to 8·0

342. TO A FRIEND
Like the evergreen so shall our friendship be ...
Some liken their love ...
$2 \cdot 0 \times 11 \cdot 0$

343. TO A FRIEND
Of all the gifts which heaven bestows ...
$1 \cdot 6 \times 6 \cdot 5$

344. TO A MOTHER
Dear mother let thy tender ...
$1 \cdot 2 \times 4 \cdot 9$ to $5 \cdot 2$

345. TO A SISTER
To my sister.
Sister dear I love thee well ...
Advertisement April 30th, 1863, no. 100.

346. TO MY BROTHER
Dear brother from infancy twined we have ...
$1 \cdot 6 \times 6 \cdot 8$

347. TO MY BROTHER
We in one mother's arms ...
$1 \cdot 7 \times 7 \cdot 2$

348. TO MY COUSIN
Peace be around thee ...
$1 \cdot 2 \times 5 \cdot 5$

349. TO MY DARLING
Mary had a little lamb ...
$1 \cdot 6 \times 7 \cdot 0$

350. TO MY DAUGHTER
At dawn of morn and close ...
$2 \cdot 1 \times 9 \cdot 1$

351. TO MY DAUGHTER
May the morn of thy existence ...
$1 \cdot 6 \times 5 \cdot 5$ to $6 \cdot 3$

352. TO MY DEAR BROTHER
But thou and I are one . . .
1·6 × 5·7 to 6·1

353. TO MY DEAR COUSIN
May blessings hover around thee . . .
To a cousin.
Dear cousin from a cousin . . .
1·6 × 5·4

354. TO MY DEAR MOTHER
On every hand . . .
1·6 × 6·3

355. TO MY DEAR SISTER
A sister's love how sweet how pure . . .
On a black ground.
2·1 × 9·6

356. TO MY DEAR SISTER
Sister is a holy name and holy . . .

357. TO MY DEAR WIFE
Our mutual bond of faith . . .
2·1 × 10·0

358. TO MY FATHER
Dear father to deserve thy love . . .
1·5 × 5·5
Advertisement Jan. 31st, 1863, no. 82.

359. TO MY FATHER
I send my love and gratitude . . .
On black and white grounds.
1·2 × 5·2 to 5·7

360. TO MY FAVOURITE
I had a little pony his name . . .
1·5 × 6·0

361. TO MY FRIEND
Of all the gifts . . .
1·6 × 7·6

362. TO MY FRIEND
To my friend.
Could I bring this lovely rose . . .
1·1 × 5·6

363. TO MY HUSBAND
May heaven's blessings be with thee . . .
2·0 × 8·8 to 9·5

364. TO MY MOTHER
Dear mother
Let thy tender care . . .
1·1 × 5·7

365. TO MY MOTHER
My mother when I was a child with . . .
2·1 × 9·4

366. TO MY PET
Dolly you're a naughty girl . . .
1·6 × 7·2

367. TO MY SISTER
There is a soft and gentle form . . .
On black and white grounds.
1·6 × 6·8 to 7·4

368. TO MY SON
Oh may the bounteous God . . .
On black and white grounds.
2·1 × 8·9 to 9·8

369. TO ONE I LOVE
Accept my heart its truthful love . .
1·5 × 5·0

370. TO ONE I LOVE
Bright be thy life and happy all thy days.
On black ground.
2·1 × 9·0

371. TO ONE I LOVE
If you are in want of . . .
On black ground.
1·6 × 6·8

372. TO ONE I LOVE
My (hand) and (heart) I offer thee oh let our (hearts) united
be.
On black and white grounds.
1·6 × 5·9 to 6·2

373. A TRIBUTE OF AFFECTION
On black ground with floral design.
1·2 × 5·2

374. A TRIBUTE OF AFFECTION
Wording in the centre with band of decoration above and
below.
1·5 × 4·9

375. A TRIBUTE OF AFFECTION
Word's utmost eloquence would fail . . .
1·6 × 5·5 to 5·8

376. TRUE LOVE
1·6 × 5·0

377. TWINKLE TWINKLE LITTLE STAR
Twinkle twinkle little star how I wonder what you are . . .
1·5 × 7·3
Design registered 283148, June 20th, 1874.

378. UNCHANGING LOVE
Though absence parts us for a while . . .
1·6 × 6·5
Design registered 157454, Nov. 15th, 1862.

379. UNCHANGING LOVE
When love is kind, cheerful and free . . .
1·6 × 6·1 to 6·5

**Queen Victoria** (380–382)

380. HER MOST GRACIOUS MAJESTY QUEEN VICTORIA
Born May 24th, 1819; Crowned June 28th, 1838.
2·1 × 11·4
Illustrated in "The Coventry Weaver", by C. J. Scott, in *The Sphere*, Nov. 8th, 1963.

381. QUEEN OF AN EMPIRE ON WHICH THE SUN NEVER SETS
1837 Jubilee 1887.
2·5 × 8·7

382. 1837 JUBILEE 1887
Victoria Queen of an empire on which the sun never sets.
1·6 × 5·4

**The Prince and Princess of Wales** (Albert Edward and Alexandra) see no. 128 ENGLAND'S JOY.

383. ENGLAND'S WELCOME TO THE PRINCESS ALEXANDRA
Sea King's daughter from over . . .
1·7 × 8·2
Advertisement Mar. 31st, 1863, no. 92.

384. GOD BLESS THE PRINCE OF WALES
Among our ancient mountains . . .
1·7 × 9·2
Advertisement Mar. 31st, 1863, no. 88.

385. HIS ROYAL HIGHNESS THE PRINCE OF WALES
1·7 × 6·5
Advertisement April 30th, 1863.
See *The Bookseller*, Jan. 31st, 1863. "Mr Stevens of Coventry has added to his collection of novel and attractive book-markers about a dozen new sorts which fully equal, if they do not surpass, those previously noticed in these columns. Trifling as these may appear we understand that they give employment to more than three hundred of the best weavers of Coventry. Among the portraits those of the Prince of Wales and his future bride, exquisitely produced on silk, will certainly become popular."

386. HER ROYAL HIGHNESS THE PRINCESS OF WALES
$1.7 \times 6.6$
Advertisement April 30th, 1863.

387. HER ROYAL HIGHNESS ALEXANDRA PRINCESS OF DENMARK
His Royal Highness Albert Edward Prince of Wales.
$1.7 \times 7.6$

388. MARRIED ST GEORGE'S CHAPEL WINDSOR MARCH 10TH 1863
Their royal Highnesses Albert Edward and Alexandra Prince and Princess of Wales.
$1.7 \times 7.6$
Advertisement Jan. 31st, 1863, no. 75.

389. PRINCE OF WALES ANTHEM
Advertisement March 31st, 1863, no. 93.

**George Washington** (390–393)

390. CENTENNIAL 1776–1876 PHILADELPHIA U.S.A.
George Washington.
And the Star Spangled Banner . . .

391. CENTENNIAL 1776–1876 U.S.A.
George Washington.
The first in peace . . .
Illustrated in *Antiques*, Vol. XXIII, 1933, p. 91, "Check List of Silk Pictures By Thomas Stevens", by Mary Dunham.

392. CENTENNIAL 1776–1876 U.S.A.
The father of our country.
The first in peace . . .
$2.0 \times 9.3$
Illustrated in *The Silk Pictures of Thomas Stevens*, by W. Baker, p. 35, fig. 2.

393. THE FATHER OF OUR COUNTRY
General George Washington.
The first in peace . . .
$2.0 \times 8.9$ to $9.2$

394. WEAVER, RICHARD
The converted collier.
1·5 × 7·1 to 7·4

395. WE PRAISE THEE O GOD
11·2 × 2·1
See no. 184 I AM THE TRUE VINE

396. WESLEY
They that be wise . . .
There are two variations:
A. With star at the pointed end.
   Design registered 152031, May 30th, 1862.
   Advertisement Oct. 31st, 1862, nos. 14 and 24.
   See no. 64 BUNYAN.
B. With roundel at the pointed end.

397. WISEMAN, CARDINAL
1·5 × 5·5 to 7·9
Design registered 153242, July 17th, 1862.
Advertisement Oct. 31st, 1862, nos. 16 and 25.
See no. 64 BUNYAN.

398. WISH, A
I will not wish thee grandeur . .
On black and white grounds.
2·0 × 9·5

399. WISH, A
I wish that happiness may . . .
1·5 × 6·1

400. WISH, A
May heavens blessing . . .
1·5 × 4·7

401. WISH, A
O may you e'er in peace abide . . .
On black and white grounds.
2·1 × 10·5 to 11·0

402. WISHING YOU A HAPPY FEAST DAY
St. Francisce Xavieri.
Ora Pro Nobis
1·6 × 5·4

403. WISHING YOU MANY HAPPY RETURNS OF THE DAY
On black ground.
1·6 × 8·0

404. WISHING YOU MANY HAPPY RETURNS OF THE DAY
Each end is pointed.
On a black ground.
2·1 × 10·7

405. WISHING YOU PEACE AND PLENTY
Give us this day our daily bread.
2·1 × 10·4 (illustration page 109)

406. WISHING YOU PROSPERITY AND PEACE
2·2 × 9·7

407. WISHING YOU VERY MUCH HAPPINESS
Bright be thy voyage o'er life's sea ...
2·1 × 10·1

408. WITH BEST WISHES
Holy Bible book divine.
There are two variations:
A. With naturalistic flowers at the pointed end. 1·6 × 6·8
B. With geometric flowers at the pointed end.
On black and white grounds. 1·6 × 6·5

409. WITH BEST WISHES
Hope the (anchor) of the soul.
The Lord bless thee and keep thee ..
2·0 × 9·0

410. WITH BEST WISHES
That health, prosperity ...
On a black ground.

411. WITH BEST WISHES
(Arabic Script.)
The Lord bless thee . . .
2·1 × 9·0

412. WITH BEST WISHES TO MY FRIEND
2·1 × 9·8'

413. WITH EVERY GOOD WISH
Design includes a portrait of Robert Burns.
2·1 × 9·0

414. WITH EVERY GOOD WISH
Sweet and peaceful be thy life . . .
1·6 × 5·5

415. WITH FOND REMEMBRANCE
1·5 × 5·5 to 5·8

416. WITH ITS MODEST VEIL SAYS YOUTH IN LOVE
WILL E'ER PREVAIL
1·6 × 5·3

417. WITH ITS PENDANT SPRAYS SHOWS WHAT SLIGHT
FEARS AFFECTION SWAYS
1·5 × 4·9

418. WITH KIND REGARDS
Bear the (cross) and wear the (crown).
1·6 × 6·0 to 6·5

419. WITH KIND REGARDS
Mizpah.
The Lord watch between . . .
On black and white grounds.
2·1 × 9·2 to 9·4

420. WITH KIND WISHES
Abide with me . . .
1·6 × 6·5

421. WITH KIND WISHES
Blessed are they that mourn for they shall be comforted.
2·1 × 9·0 to 10·1

422. WITH KIND WISHES
I send . . .
On a black ground.
1·2 × 6·2

423. WITH SINCERE WISHES FOR YOUR HAPPINESS
On black and white grounds.
2·1 × 9·4 to 9·6

424. XAVIER, ST. FRANCIS
1·7 × 5·0

425. XAVIER, THE DEATH OF ST. FRANCIS
1·6 × 5·5

426. YORK MINSTER FROM THE SOUTH EAST
His grace the Archbishop of York.
St. Mary's Abbey.
Each ivi'd arch . . .
10·8 × 2·0
See the *Yorkshire Gazette*, September 29th, 1886. "We have
already referred to the Exhibition ribbons which are worked
in this loom and present admirable likenesses of the Archbishop and the Lord Mayor with architectural illustrations."
See *Yorkshire Fine Art and Industrial Exhibition Catalogue*,
1866, No. 693, "Stevens, T.—Jacquard Ribbon loom, articles
produced by this loom are on sale at the adjoining stall".

*The following bookmarkers were examined too late to be included
in the general catalogue.*

427. BE JUST AND FEAR NOT
On blue ground.
0·5 × 6·3

428. BRIGHT, THE APOSTLE OF FREE TRADE
The eloquent . . .

429. CHAPEL STREET OLD CHAPEL BLACKBURN
Founded 1778. Enlarged 1811 . . .
Design includes a list of ministers and a picture of the
Congregational Church.
2·2 × 9·8

430. COMPLIMENTS OF THE SEASON, THE
$1.5 \times 4.5$

431. COMPLIMENTS OF THE SEASON, THE
I wish the newly coming year . . .
$1.3 \times 5.5$

432. FORGIVE AND FORGET
On blue ground.
$0.5 \times 6.5$

433. FROM YOUR FRIEND
Should auld acquaintance . . .
With Good Wishes.
$2.3 \times 9.8$

434. GLADSTONE, RT. HON. W. E.
The Champion of Liberty.
$1.5 \times 4.0$

435. KNOX
Knox preaching at St Andrews.
He put down . . .

436. PRAY WITHOUT CEASING
Narrow band on red ground.

437. SOUVENIR OF THE DISCOVERY OF AMERICA
Landing of Columbus.
Columbus.
The Santa Maria.
$2.5 \times 9.3$
Made at the 1893 Chicago Exposition.

438. SOUVENIR OF THE INDEPENDENCE OF AMERICA
George Washington first President of the United States.
Signing of the Declaration of Independence July 4th 1776.
Victory.
$9.0 \times 2.5$

STG 154

STG 187

STG 189

STG 107            STG 109

STG 129

While stocks last, copies of this book can be
obtained from Michael Darby

# INDEX TO PART I

## Section 1. PORTRAITS

European Royalty and Notables all appear on page 51.

## Section 2. PICTURES

## ADVERTISERS' ANNOUNCEMENTS

# NOTES

# NOTES

# NOTES

# NOTES